THE RETURN
OF THE STAR
OF BETHLEHEM

THE RETURN
OF THE STAR
OF BETHLEHEM

KENNETH BOA
AND
WILLIAM PROCTOR

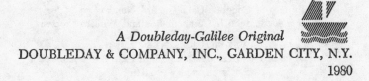

A Doubleday-Galilee Original
DOUBLEDAY & COMPANY, INC., GARDEN CITY, N.Y.
1980

ISBN: 0-385-15454-2
Library of Congress Catalog Card Number 79-8548
Copyright © 1980 by Kenneth Boa and William Proctor

To our wives, Karen and Pam

CONTENTS

THE RETURN
OF THE STAR
OF BETHLEHEM

PART ONE

A STAR
IN THE EAST

CHAPTER ONE

A MESSAGE
IN THE SKIES

It could have all started on a planet in the solar system of a galaxy three thousand light-years away.

There may even have been an intelligent civilization on that planet.

Assume for a moment that the people in this faraway civilization looked and behaved something like we earthlings, except that they had advanced far beyond us in their personal relationships, their governmental system, their artistic achievements and their technological capabilities. Life for them was what we would call comfortable, peaceful, even happy. There was no poverty, racial injustice or class oppression. They had gained wisdom from the successes and failures of their previous generations, and they could afford to smile confidently at the future.

At least they could smile until their highly trained scientists confronted them with the unthinkable: their sun was about to explode and annihilate all that they had striven so hard to achieve. There was no hope of escape. Everyone and everything would die.

At first, no one could believe it. Their civilization, now at its zenith, would no longer even exist within a few weeks. There would be no legacy, no future generations to enjoy the fruits of their labor. Then, as the terminal diagnosis for this intelligent race began to sink in, there was anger, frustration and finally, resignation. In a last and probably futile gesture to save something of their way of life, they built a huge vault on the most distant planet in their solar system and sealed their most valuable records and treasures deep within.

Then, the unthinkable became reality. To the ordinary individual on this highly advanced planet, there was little warning except for an increasing brightness of their sun's light. But the cataclysm accelerated swiftly after that. First, the sunlight became painful to the eyes, no matter where they tried to look. Then the heat became more and more unbearable. Within an hour, the planets closer to the sun were already being burned to a crisp. Finally, the holocaust consumed this intelligent civilization and all its achievements. All that remained was a pitiful, charred little vault on a distant planet in a dead solar system.

But that was not the end, for the light generated by the exploding sun still lived. It increased a billionfold in brilliance within a few hours and emitted more light than all the other suns in the entire galaxy combined. The incredible flame and light lasted for several weeks. The devastation from the blast was largely limited to the original doomed solar system, but the light, moving at incredible speed out into the universe, reached other nearby solar systems after four or five years of travel, and lighted the planets whirling around these solar systems with a ball of flame in the heavens that rivaled their own suns.

The light from the supernova—for that is what we would call the explosion of that sun—continued to move at high speed throughout the rest of the universe, though the brilliance waned the farther it got from its source. Three thousand years after the initial explosion, in the destroyed solar system that had been the home of that highly advanced civilization, the buried vault containing the records and wisdom of that extinct race lay unopened and undiscovered. But the light from the cosmic blast had reached another planet with another civilization—one which was not quite so advanced but which nevertheless saw a special message in the light that shone down upon their world.

The more primitive planet was earth. The light from the supernova lasted for several weeks and rivaled the planet Venus in brightness. A group of Magi interpreted this mysterious new star as a sign signaling the birth of the King of the Jews. So they set out on a journey that eventually led them to the child Jesus.

This story is complete fantasy, of course, and is essentially the scenario painted by author Arthur C. Clarke in a scientific essay and also in his science fiction short story "Supernova Bethlehem."[1] But Clarke's interpretation of the Star of Bethlehem shows how that long-ago event has captured the imagination of scientists, theologians and other creative thinkers up to the present day.

Although there are almost as many different theories on the Star as there are individuals, everyone seems to agree on at least one thing: Nearly two thousand years ago, something incredible happened in the heavens. The event was so startling that it riveted the attention of a number of ancient gurus and drew them, as one man, to a seemingly insignificant little town in the Eastern Mediterranean.

The Magi, or wise men, as they are widely known today, interpreted the light as a divine message in the skies, but what exactly was it that they saw? And what was the full significance of the Star that so dazzled them?

Here are a few responses from expert observers, both past and present:

• The Star may have been a nova or supernova, an explosion in deep space, as Arthur C. Clarke so vividly depicts in his writings.

• It may have been a meteor or meteor shower, which

might have consisted of two hundred thousand meteors emerging from a single point in the sky over a short period of time.

· It could have been a bolide or huge fireball of the type that could have created the huge crater in Arizona and the devastation of a forest in Siberia.

· Some believe that the unusual light the Magi followed was caused by one heavenly body, as in a solar or lunar eclipse or in the particularly prominent appearance of a single bright star, such as Sirius, or a planet, such as Venus.

· The Star might have been a conjunction of planets that had special meaning to astrologers of the day.

· It may have been a comet, with a tail seemingly pointing the way to Bethlehem and the Messiah.

· Some theorists also argue that the Star of Bethlehem was actually an unidentified flying object (UFO) sent by a super-intelligent civilization from outer space.

Each of these interpretations has its advocates, and each has something to commend it. But there are also some problems with all of these speculations. For example, if the Star really involved a generally visible happening in the heavens, why does Matthew say in his Gospel, which is our only description of the event, that Herod had to ask the wise men when the heavenly body appeared? Also, what kind of heavenly body would tend to appear, disappear and then reappear, as the Star apparently did? And is there any record of a star, meteor, comet or any other object in the skies that had a directional and guided "beam" that would point out the spot where the child Jesus lay?

In the ensuing pages, we'll examine each of the current theories about the nature of the Star. Then, using this information as a backdrop, we'll try to penetrate the true nature and meaning of this startling event that happened so long ago, yet still affects us profoundly today. For you see, the Star of Bethlehem was not just an astronomical curiosity or a fantastic, alien-world phenomenon, but something much more serious. Far from being a one-time cosmological event, the so-called Star that the Magi saw and followed was the first foray in a cosmic chain of events that will make the intergalactic confrontations in stories like *Star Wars* seem like child's play.

CHAPTER TWO

GURUS FROM THE EAST

The scene is a familiar one in films and pop art: One Caucasian king rides on a litter borne by servants from a northern kingdom, presumably somewhere in Europe. Another king, with more Semitic features, journeys from some Oriental land with enough armed escorts and other attendants to populate a small nation. The third king, a majestic-looking black man, is being fanned by slaves as he embarks on a long journey from some African country.

The dress and entourage of each king are so opulent that bystanders are awestruck as each of the processions passes by. The three groups finally meet on a road just to the east of Jerusalem, and they march together into the city with such an impressive display that all activity seems to come to a stop. During all this fanfare, of course, a huge star gleams in the heavens.

This is the picture that popular writers have given us of the Magi, or "wise men," of Matthew's Gospel. Unfortunately, these depictions are mostly unsubstantiated fiction. They contradict not only the Bible but also much of the other known historical evidence surrounding the Bethlehem Star.

If our search for the Star is to prove successful, we have to

stick strictly to the facts. And the facts are that there *may*
have been three Magi; but the similarity to the above Cecil B.
de Mille scenario ends at that point.

Still, an understanding of the identity of the Magi is crucial
to any understanding of the Star. Precisely what sort of light
did they see in the heavens and why were they motivated to
follow it? That question can only be answered by first strip-
ping away the popular misconceptions and somewhat mysterious aura surrounding them. Here is the relevant passage from
the Gospel of Matthew, chapter 2, verses 1–16, which provides
the only known description of the Magi and the Star of Bethlehem:

> After Jesus was born in Bethlehem in Judea, dur-
> ing the time of King Herod, Magi from the east came
> to Jerusalem and asked, "Where is the one who has
> been born king of the Jews? We saw his star in the
> east and have come to worship him."
>
> When King Herod heard this he was disturbed,
> and all Jerusalem with him. When he had called to-
> gether all the people's chief priests and teachers of
> the law, he asked them where the Christ was to be
> born. "In Bethlehem in Judea," they replied, "for
> this is what the prophet has written:
>
> > 'And you, Bethlehem, in the land of Judah,
> > are by no means least among the rulers of Judah;
> > for out of you will come a ruler
> > who will be the shepherd of my people Israel.'"
>
> Then Herod called the Magi secretly and found
> out from them the exact time the star had appeared.
> He sent them to Bethlehem and said, "Go and make
> a careful search for the child. As soon as you find
> him, report to me, so that I too may go and worship
> him."
>
> After they had heard the king, they went on their

way, and the star they had seen in the east went ahead of them until it stopped over the place where the child was. When they saw the star, they were overjoyed. On coming to the house, they saw the child with his mother Mary, and they bowed down and worshiped him. Then they opened their treasures and presented him with gifts of gold and of incense and of myrrh. And having been warned in a dream not to go back to Herod, they returned to their country by another route.

When they had gone, an angel of the Lord appeared to Joseph in a dream. "Get up," he said, "take the child and his mother and escape to Egypt. Stay there until I tell you, for Herod is going to search for the child to kill him."

So he got up, took the child and his mother during the night and left for Egypt, where he stayed until the death of Herod. And so was fulfilled what the Lord had said through the prophet: "Out of Egypt I called my son."

When Herod realized that he had been outwitted by the Magi, he was furious, and he gave orders to kill all the boys in Bethlehem and its vicinity who were two years old and under, in accordance with the time he had learned from the Magi. (New International Version)

The Magi, or wise men, as other translations of the Bible call them, were the only recorded individuals who saw the Star. It was their report that caused Herod to launch a massive search to locate and kill the Christ child. But who, exactly, were these Magi? Where did they come from? And, most important, what is the significance of their identity in our search for the Star?

First of all, whoever these Magi were, they lived during a period when there was a widespread sense of messianic expectation, or an anticipation that some great political and spiritual deliverer was about to appear. The Roman historian Suetonius wrote, "There had spread over all the Orient an old and established belief, that it was fated at that time for men coming from Judaea to rule the world."[1]

The Jewish literature of the time was filled with prophecies and predictions about the coming of the Messiah. The book of Daniel was a basic Old Testament messianic text; but there was also a widespread dissemination of nonbiblical works such as the Book of Enoch, the Jewish Sibylline books, and the Apocalypse of Baruch, all of which dealt with the coming of the Savior of the Jewish people. In fact, so intense was the feeling that the time was ripe for the Messiah that no fewer than three false messiahs arose during that general era. They were "Judas the Galilean"; a former slave of Herod; and a man named Athrongeus. Each wore a crown and aspired to the throne of Judea, according to the ancient Jewish historian Josephus.[2]

A similar kind of spiritual expectation gripped many in the Parthian, or Persian, Empire, just to the east of Palestine in what is now Iran. An important part of Persian religious beliefs was the idea that a great prophet or savior would appear in the last days to save mankind from evil and hardship. And life was certainly no bed of roses in Persia during the first century B.C. King Phraates IV, who reigned there from 37 to 2 B.C., was one of the most cruel despots of the day. His rule was marked by nearly constant war against Roman troops led by Marc Antony and Augustus Caesar, and he also fought against rebels in his own kingdom and nearby neighbors who refused to put up with his terrible acts.

So in Judea as well as in surrounding lands, there was an intense desire for some savior who would deliver the people from their poverty and pain. The Magi were probably part of this general milieu, and they would have shared the same sense of messianic expectation.

But who were they and where did they come from?

Matthew says only that they came from the "east," and that could mean any of a number of locations. There are arguments that they were Arabians, Babylonians, Essenes, Indian Buddhists and Persians. Here are some of the considerations for each of these possibilities:

1. *Arabians*. If you had headed east from the ancient land of Palestine (present-day Israel), you would have first encountered the Syro-Arabian desert, then the land of Babylon in Mesopotamia and finally Persia. The most ancient sources say—and one of the most popular views today is—that the Magi came from Arabia and that there's no need to look any farther east.

There are three basic reasons that are given for this conclusion: First of all, the gifts that the Magi gave Jesus—gold, incense (or frankincense) and myrrh—are said to be especially characteristic of the Arabians. But that's not entirely true.[3] Gold, for example, was a life-giving, death-defying metal in the view of the Egyptians. Frankincense, the resinous fluid from certain Middle Eastern trees, was abundant not only in southwest Arabia, but also in Abyssinia and India. The ancient Hebrews used it in worship, too. Myrrh, also a resinous secretion from trees, was present not only in Arabia, but in many other parts of the Middle East. The Jews, for example, used it as a holy anointing oil and a cosmetic, and it was also used as part of a drug offered to Christ on Calvary and as a spice at His burial.

The second reason that Arabia is the favorite of many people as the home of the Magi is the nearness of that land to Jerusalem and Bethlehem. There is a tradition that the Star *accompanied* Christ's birth and that the visit of the Magi was on the twelfth day after the nativity. If this dating is correct, it would have taken much too long for travelers to reach Bethlehem from Babylon or Persia. But there's no hard evidence that this tradition is anything more than unsubstantiated legend. The Gospel of Matthew, our main source de-

scribing the Magi and the Star, says nothing about any visit
on the twelfth day, nor do any other reliable early historical
sources.

The third argument favoring Arabia is that the language of
the Arabians and their customs were more similar to the traditions of ancient Palestine than to those of other countries. The
Arabians could have made themselves understood to the Ara-
maic-speaking Jews more easily than the Persians, for example, who spoke stranger Indo-European dialects. Also, the argument goes, the Arabians would have been more likely to be
aware of the messianic prophecy of the Old Testament figure
Balaam, in Numbers 24:17: "a star will come out of Jacob, a
scepter will rise out of Israel. . . ." (NIV)

But this is all rather weak evidence to make Arabia the
leading candidate for the home of the Magi. Intelligent people of every age have been multilingual when circumstances
required—or at least they are adept at selecting an effective
interpreter. And passages from the Hebrew Scriptures would
have been known in many lands other than Arabia. So it's necessary to look farther east for the country of the wise men.

2. *Babylonians.* The Babylonians, or Chaldeans, as they
were also called, occupied the deserts between northern Arabia and the Persian Gulf. They are much more likely candidates for the Magi nationality because they were known as expert astronomers and ardent astrologers. If the Star of
Bethlehem was actually a star, a planet or some other heavenly body, the Babylonians would have been among the first
to discern its significance and head for Palestine.

Many of the peoples living at the time of the birth of Christ
believed that the birth and death of great individuals were
marked by unusual events in the sky, such as the appearance
of comets, new stars or conjunctions of certain key planets. In
fact, they assumed that everything on earth was just a reaction to what took place in the heavens. So an understanding of
the stars was essential for those who wanted to predict the fu-

ture and discern the true meaning of life, including the will of their key god or pantheon of gods.

The astrologers of those days, who assumed an especially important role in times of hardship or apocalyptic expectation, believed that the planet Saturn represented earthly kings. Jupiter was also a heavenly body associated with royalty. So when a conjunction, or drawing together, of Jupiter and Saturn occurred in 7 B.C., those in the stargazing professions could be expected to have become quite excited. And a number of Biblical scholars believe that 7 B.C. may well have been the actual year in which Christ was born.

Babylonia, then, is definitely a front-runner among the nations which may have been the homeland of the Magi. But there are other considerations, as we'll shortly see, which may place the wise men's origins in a different location.

3. The Essenes. A few people believe that the wise men of the nativity scene came from the Qumran community of Jewish monks who lived in the caves on the western shores of the Dead Sea. They were interested in trying to predict the future and were fascinated about speculations on the "star of Jacob," which the Old Testament prophet Balaam mentioned in his oracle in the Book of Numbers. They also practiced astronomy, so they would have been aware of unusual events that occurred in the Judean skies.

The problem with this view is that there is no solid historical evidence for it, either in the documents of the day or in Matthew's account. In fact, the clear implication in Matthew is that the Magi came from another country, not another part of Palestine. Also, they apparently had a much more deficient knowledge of Hebrew Scripture prophecies and geography than the Essenes would have had because the Magi had to seek guidance from Herod in Jerusalem.

4. Indian Buddhists. Although such a faraway origin for the Magi may at first glance seem farfetched, there is some basis for this theory. One Eastern scholar, Vladas Stanka, has drawn some parallels between the search for a new Dalai Lama, the spiritual ruler of Tibet, and the search of the wise men for the Christ child.[4] It seems that after one Dalai Lama died, a group of Tibetan "wise men" would go out to look for a child who had received the soul of the deceased Dalai Lama. Stanka concedes that Lamaism didn't appear in Tibet until the sixth or seventh century A.D., and that the method of selecting the Dalai Lama evolved centuries after that. But he argues that the Buddhist roots of Lamaism, which go back many years before the birth of Christ, have elements reminiscent of the Star of Bethlehem incident in Matthew.

He says, for example, that he believes the teachings of Jesus and Gautama Buddha, who founded that early Buddhist faith, are alike in many ways. A tradition arose in Buddhism that a great "Celestial Wheel" with a thousand spokes appeared in the sky, and that when the Wheel revealed itself completely to some righteous king, he would become sovereign of the world. Certain early inscriptions in India connect the Celestial Wheel story and the appearance of a righteous king to a historical Indian ruler, Asoka, who became king in 270 or 272 B.C. He issued a series of edicts as part of his Dharma, or "The Good Law," which extolled good deeds, compassion, liberality, truthfulness and purity.

Asoka sent out envoys to other parts of the world to proclaim his views about the Good Law, and the Buddhist tale of the Celestial Wheel came to represent these efforts symbolically. Stanka concludes that, even though Asoka lived much earlier than the birth of Christ, there may thus be a connection between Asoka's Celestial Wheel and the Star, which heralded the birth of the Prince of love and peace.

This theory has some interesting elements, but it's the least substantial of all those proposed. The chronological discrepancy between the dates of Asoka's reign and Christ's birth remove the Buddhist interpretation of the wise men and the

Star from the realm of historical reality. And the very purpose of the Magi in Matthew contradicts Asoka's envoys. The Magi came to find and worship the new king, while Asoka's men were spreading the good word about a king who already existed. So it's necessary to look beyond these fanciful notions to the most likely theory of all about the Magi—the conclusion that they came from Persia, or present-day Iran.

5. *Persian Wise Men.* There is more to be said for placing the origins of the Magi in Persia than in any other ancient land. The ancient Greek historian Herodotus noted back in the fifth century B.C. that the Magi were one of the tribes of the Median peoples (or the Persians, as we also know them).[5] These Magi were a priestly caste, like the Druids for the Celts or the tribe of Levi for the Hebrews. The name "Magi" came to refer to a priestly or magical profession, rather than exclusively to a particular nationality, but the roots remained in Persia.

The Magi had a reputation as great masters of learning—even the Greek philosopher Plato was eager to visit and study with them. But gradually, the image of these "wise men" as an intellectual elite changed as more of them got involved in secret and mysterious arts, astrology, magic and the occult. The Jews and early Christians believed that it was a bad idea to get involved with sorcerer-type Magi because they consorted with evil spirits and other satanic supernatural forces that were in league against Christ and the good heavenly hosts. In fact, the only other use of the word "Magi" in the New Testament is in Acts 13:6, 8, where it is translated "magician" and used to describe Bar-Jesus, a false Jewish prophet.

But despite the negative aura attached to some Magi, those in Persia seem to have maintained a higher level of integrity and a greater stress on scholarly learning, rather than black magic. The image of the Magi in Matthew is quite positive, so it seems reasonable to assume that they were priestly intellectuals who had managed to maintain the highest standards of their profession.

The Magi, as the intellects of their day in Persia, would also have been acquainted with astrology and other fields of knowledge that dealt with the stars. Astrology—the belief that the movement of stars and planets affects our individual destinies—and astronomy were closely connected in ancient times, and any well-educated person would have known something about each.

But unlike the Arabians and Babylonians, whose main religious interest was astrology, the Persian faith centered on a belief in Zoroaster, an ancient Persian prophet whose origins are uncertain but whom some historians have identified as the founder of the Magi caste around 1000 B.C.

At the time of Christ's birth, Zoroastrian priests in Persia taught that there was one supreme god, and they kept no altars or statues in their temples. They believed there were two creators in the universe, one good and one evil, and these two forces were in continual conflict. The good spirit was expected to win this battle, but before the triumph, the forces of evil would rally and it would be necessary for the good spirit to send a Savior—or Sosiosh—to achieve the final victory. This Savior, the Zoroastrians believed, would be born supernaturally of a virgin, heal the world of all its strife and then reign a thousand years.[6]

From this brief summary of Zoroastrianism, it's obvious that there were many similarities between the Persian expectations of a Savior and the actual coming of the Hebrew Messiah. So if the "wise men" in the Gospel were actually Persian Magi, they could very naturally move into an acceptance of Jesus as the Savior of the world.

There is also other strong evidence of the Persian origins of the Magi. Artwork on the walls of the catacombs, where the early Christians met and sometimes hid themselves in the Roman world during dangerous periods, shows depictions of the wise men with a special pointed headdress, which might also be called the "Phrygian cap," or the "cap of liberty." They are also shown wearing a short tunic, a short cloak called a chlamys and shoes with a distinctive kind of stocking. This costume is reminiscent of the Persian national dress of that day.[7]

It's unlikely, then, that the Magi who arrived in ancient Palestine nearly two thousand years ago were the "three kings of Orient" that we sing about in our Christmas carols. Some have made the wise men into kings by applying Old Testament passages such as Psalm 72:10 and Isaiah 49:7 to them. But it's more likely they were Persian priests, well versed in astrology and astronomy, but also steeped in the messianic expectations of Zoroastrianism. They might have had little or no entourage and may even have been on foot as they walked with relatively little fanfare toward Jerusalem.

Now is as good a time as any to deal with a few other popular misconceptions. Although many Christmas cards show the shepherds worshiping the Christ child with the wise men beside them and the Star of Bethlehem in the background, in fact the shepherds never saw this particular star. Also, the Magi came along later than the shepherds—perhaps several months later—and they saw Jesus in a house, not a manger.

The number of the wise men is also uncertain, despite the fact that we've always heard about the "three kings." They brought three gifts, gold, incense and myrrh, and so it was apparently assumed at an early date that there must have been one wise man for each gift. But some Syrian writers have argued there were actually twelve Magi, and other speculations put the number at four or two. The weight of Western church tradition has kept the number at three since the mid-second century.[8]

They were given the names Gaspar, Melchior and Balthasar in the sixth century, but that decision seems to have no basis in historic fact. Also, the idea that they represented the European, Semitic and African ethnic groups—and the next logical inference, that one of them was black—is pure fantasy.

The best conclusion is that if you could have stood on the walls of Jerusalem about two thousand years ago—on precisely the right day and hour—you would not have seen three opulently clothed and adorned "kings" moving majestically toward the city from different directions with a veritable army of attendants. Instead, you would probably have seen three or more men with distinctive pointed hats and peculiar cloaks and tunics, perhaps traveling on foot with a small number of attendants, if there were any at all. There would have been little if any attention paid to them—maybe just some mild interest because they were foreigners.

A brief conversation would have disclosed they were quite well-educated Persian priests who were well acquainted with astrology and the study of the heavens, but who also had a deep faith in Zoroastrianism—especially the conviction that the time was ripe for the coming of a Savior, or Sosiosh, who would be born in some supernatural way of a virgin. They would have told you they had seen "his star in the East" and now they're in a hurry to locate and worship Him. Their educational background would have put you on notice that the Star they claimed to have seen could have been any number of things—an astronomical oddity such as a meteor, an astrological portent such as a conjunction, or something completely supernatural which their Persian beliefs might have prepared them to accept.

But you would not have seen the Star. In fact, no one in Jerusalem would know what they were talking about at first because there had been no reports of unusual or important astronomical events in the heavens. But they would have kept pressing you and anyone else they could get to listen, and gradually the word would have gotten around that these fellows from the Persian Magi caste were in town and were creating something of a stir.

The fact that they were asking about the birth of a "Savior" or a "King of the Jews" in terms of their own Zoroastrian faith may have seemed rather strange. But they were obviously men of intelligence and their search for the "Sosiosh" sounded enough like the Hebrew notion of the Messiah to make more than one Jewish scholar sit up and take notice.

So it was not the extravagant appearance of these Magi nor their impressive entourage, but rather their provocative and disturbing questions that finally got the attention of King Herod.

CHAPTER THREE
THE EVIL KING

As the Persian Magi walked over to Herod's palace, it's interesting to speculate about what may have been on their minds.

They may have been excited about the prospect of pooling their knowledge with that of Herod's priestly advisers and perhaps collaborating in the search for the Messiah. Or they may have been baffled by the special attention being shown them by Herod the Great. After all, this king of Judea and the surrounding lands was a noted monarch who had received the special support of the Roman conquerors Antony and Octavian.

More likely, though, they were simply afraid. The Magi must have known something about Herod's reputation as a paranoid, cruel and probably insane ruler, and his reported unpredictability may have had them shaking in their boots.

Actually, Herod the Great was in many ways just another petty Roman procurator—a good bit more evil than most, but not particularly worth our time except for one key fact: The date of his death is of supreme importance both in determining the date of Christ's birth and also in our search for the Star of Bethlehem. Both of those events must have occurred before Herod died, according to Matthew's account, so brace yourself for a more intimate acquaintance with one of the great bad guys of all time.

Herod was born in 73 B.C. and became governor of the Galilee province when he was only twenty-five years old. He was a half-Jew with an Edomite ancestry, and his father, Antipater, was a successful military leader and procurator under Julius Caesar. Marc Antony was so impressed with Herod that he promoted him to tetrarch in 42 B.C. The Roman Senate, at the urging of Antony and Octavian (later called Augustus Caesar), eventually proclaimed him the "King of the Jews."

This lofty designation was somewhat less than it might seem, though, because even though Herod had the title, he didn't have the kingdom. His Roman overlords were acutely aware that the soldiers of the Parthian Empire had invaded Syria and Palestine and installed Antigonus of the Hasmonean family as king of Judea in 40 B.C. The ambitious young Herod seemed a likely candidate to throw the Parthians back out of the area, so the Roman Senate gave him the kingly title and in effect said, "Now, Herod, go earn it!"

Herod did conquer his kingdom, and he finally captured Jerusalem in 37 B.C. But that was only the beginning of his headaches. He decided to try to consolidate his position in Judea by marrying Mariamne, a member of the Hasmonean family that he had displaced. But the older Herod got, the more insanely suspicious he became. Some have attributed his growing paranoia to a progressive hardening of the arteries—a process which may have affected his brain. On the other hand, there were enough concrete threats to his power to justify much of his fear and uncertainty. Cleopatra, for example, always had her eye on Judea, and it wasn't until she lost the Battle of Actium that her threat was removed.

Whatever the reality of the dangers to his power, Herod lashed out violently to destroy any hint of an enemy presence. He murdered his wife Mariamne and her mother Alexandra and also killed his eldest son, Antipater, and two other sons, Alexander and Aristobulus. Herod's reputation for hostility to his family became so widely known that Augustus himself once said he would rather be Herod's hog than his son—an allusion to the Jewish aversion for the flesh of swine.

Nor was Herod's savagery limited to his family. The Jewish-Roman historian Josephus reported that when Herod was about to die, he decided he wanted to have some company when he left this world. So he ordered that one member of each household in his kingdom should be killed—though fortunately this command was not carried out.

Such brutality makes it easier to understand the incident Matthew records in his Gospel, when Herod ordered that all the male children in Bethlehem two years old and under be executed. Since Bethlehem was a small town, the number of infants destroyed would probably have been in the range of ten to twenty-five individuals—a small figure considering that early writers often estimated mass killings in the thousands.

With this background in mind, then, the Magi may well have been somewhat uncomfortable as they entered the palace for their audience with Herod the Great. If they feared for anything at this point, though, it was probably only their own safety. There is no indication from Matthew's account that they suspected that Herod had any designs on the life of the newborn Messiah. But of course that's exactly what was on the evil king's mind. He had already assembled his chief priests and teachers of the law so that he could refresh his memory about the Biblical prophecies on the Messiah. The advisers quoted some words from the Old Testament prophet Micah that the Savior was supposed to be born in Bethlehem, and this information gave Herod the leverage he expected he would need to do some horse trading with the Magi.

Herod's motives were clear: He wanted to learn where the purported Messiah was and then kill Him. But he knew he would have little success with this plan if the wise men got wind of his intentions. So he got in touch with them secretly— probably because he knew that the inhabitants of Jerusalem understood his cruel nature better than these foreigners and might warn the Magi away before he even got a chance to speak with them.

It's evident from Matthew's brief account of their conversation that some give and take took place. Herod asked them about the Star they had seen—a heavenly phenomenon that neither he nor his advisers had witnessed. Then he told them about the Bethlehem prophecy and sent them to the town with the instruction, "Go and make a careful search for the child. As soon as you find him, report to me, so that I too may go and worship him."

Herod was a wily fellow, and there's no hint that at this stage the Magi suspected he had evil designs on the infant. As a matter of fact, the Magi would probably have volunteered what they knew about the Star without insisting on any *quid pro quo* from Herod. But Herod was a devious, I'll-scratch-your-back-if-you'll-scratch-mine kind of person, and he never would have expected something for nothing from anybody else. Also, he probably realized that foreign priests searching for a Savior would arouse less suspicion than his own attendants or soldiers.

So as the Magi left Herod and headed toward the nearby town of Bethlehem, the mysterious Star appeared again before them and directed them in some unexplained way to the house where Jesus was staying with Mary and Joseph. They worshiped Him there and presented Him with their gifts of gold, incense and myrrh. But then they were warned in a dream not to return to Herod, so they traveled back to their own country by another route.

Herod, predictably, was enraged when he learned that the Magi had seen through his plan to kill the child. He ordered that all the boys in Bethlehem two years old and younger be killed, but Jesus and his parents had already escaped to Egypt after being warned in a dream. They stayed in Egypt until Herod died and then journeyed to Nazareth.

But when, exactly, did Herod die? This is an important question because the date of his death is a key factor in determining what was going on in the heavens during those ancient times—and whether those astronomical events have any clear message for us about the identity of the Star of Bethlehem. For example, if a dramatic supernova or comet lighted up the heavens several years *after* Herod's death, that fact may be of some interest to astronomers but it has little relevance to our search for the Star. Whatever happened in the sky must have happened *before* Herod died, because the only account of the Magi's observation of the Star took place while he was still living.

The ancient historian Josephus says that Herod reigned for thirty-seven years after he was named king of Judaea in 40 B.C.[1] That leads us to the year 4 B.C. as the date of his death, and many contemporary historians agree with this conclusion. There's also some other evidence to support this year for his death: Ancient sources say that an eclipse of the moon occurred in the year of Herod's death; and shortly after he died, the Jewish Passover observance was postponed by his son and successor, Archelaus, as a mourning observance. Both an eclipse and a postponed Passover occurred in 4 B.C., and that seems to settle the matter.[2]

The evidence points even more precisely to a likely death for Herod in the spring, and perhaps late March, of 4 B.C. But to answer our main question—the date of the Star—we next have to determine when Jesus was born and finally when the Magi arrived to worship Him.

There are a number of theories on the time of Jesus' birth, but the one which seems most likely would bring Him into the world around December of 5 B.C. or January of 4 B.C. And here's one personal comment at this point: We're not being unduly influenced by the traditional date of December 25 for Christmas! All sentiment aside, there are some good, solid reasons for a winter birth date for Christ.

First of all, there must have been enough time between the date of Christ's birth and Herod's death for Jesus to have been taken to Jerusalem for the traditional purification rites on the fortieth day after His birth; for Mary and Joseph to have moved from the manger to a house in Bethlehem; for the Magi to have visited; and for Joseph to have escaped with his family to Egypt. These Biblical events must have taken a minimum of two months and probably a little longer. So, counting back from Herod's death in late March of 4 B.C., you end up in January or perhaps late December for the birth of Jesus. The Star, then, probably appeared to the Magi in 5 B.C. or early in 4 B.C., before Herod died.

None of these attempts at dating can be absolutely accurate, of course, because some of the ancient sources we rely on, such as Josephus, may have been slightly off, and the Bible doesn't mention specific dates. It's possible, for example, that the birth of Christ may have occurred as early as 8 or 7 B.C. because the census of Quirinius mentioned in Luke 2:1-6 may have occurred as early as that date. Although there have been conflicting arguments about when Quirinius was in charge of Palestine, Syria and other parts of the Middle East, the latest findings show he exercised considerable control in those regions from as early as 12 B.C. to as late as A.D. 16. There is a recorded census under him in A.D. 6 and none before the death of Herod, but the practice in those days was to have ongoing census projects, usually every fourteen years, with special early registrations and other preliminary procedures. This is the sort of thing that may well have happened in the neighborhood of 8 to 7 B.C., and which Luke records just prior to Jesus' birth.[3]

So keep in mind this possible early date of 8 or 7 B.C. for Christ's birth along with the later, and in many ways preferable, date of 4 B.C. That way, we'll have a more reasonable range of time to explore what exactly went on in the skies above Bethlehem.

Now, the cast of characters in our little drama is almost complete. We know something about the nature of the Magi and the evil King Herod, and we also have a good notion about when Jesus arrived in the flesh. But it's necessary to say "almost complete" because one of the major actors in this event of nearly two thousand years ago is still clouded in mystery. The unknown quantity is the Star itself, because this light in the skies was in many ways an independent force with a kind of personality all its own. Whatever it was, it became a beacon that helped change the course of history. And if certain theories about it are correct, we may not have seen the last of it.

But before we launch into a full-blown discussion of the identity of the Star of Bethlehem, let's first be sure about where we stand with the manuscript evidence we'll be using. If you're a Christian and you believe that the account of the Star in Matthew's Gospel is authoritative and accurate, then you should have no problem following the line of reasoning in the rest of this book. But if you have problems with the Bible —if you think Matthew's story of the Magi is just a myth or fantasy—this is a good time to introduce you to a couple of keys to ancient mysteries that may change your mind.

CHAPTER FOUR

THE KEYS TO
ANCIENT MYSTERIES

Was there really a Star of Bethlehem? Or was it just the figment of some overzealous early Christian's imagination?

If we believed it was only a fantasy, this would be a much shorter book. But these are good questions to raise at this point in our search for the Star, especially if you're inclined to be skeptical about the events described in the Bible.

If you are a person who wants to conduct a serious exploration of ancient phenomena like the Star, there are a couple of hardheaded, scientific queries you should pose at the outset, just to be sure it's worth your while to continue the investigation. First of all, you should be sure that the ancient manuscripts you'll be reading to learn about the Star are reliable. And secondly, you should know the full meaning of the important ancient words in those manuscripts. For our purposes, this means it's absolutely essential to understand the actual meaning of the word "star" at the time that Matthew wrote it.

Let's deal in turn with each of these keys to the ancient mystery of the Star.

1. *Are the manuscripts of Matthew's Gospel reliable?* Much has been written about how solid and truthful the

books of the New Testament are. Many Biblical scholars and theologians have concluded that, apart from considerations of faith, they are actually much more reliable than most other ancient writings we accept as "gospel" in our universities today.

The main reason for this conclusion is that the New Testament documents, including those containing the Gospel of Matthew, pass with flying colors the tests that scholars have set down for determining the authenticity of ancient texts. Here are some of the reasons why Biblical scholars such as F. F. Bruce[1] and others are willing to put the New Testament, including Matthew, among the most historically trustworthy of all ancient records:

• Matthew was written sometime between A.D. 65 and 90, according to a variety of Biblical scholars. This means that the actual drafting of the original manuscript would have been done during a period when many of the eyewitnesses to events in the life of Jesus were still alive. The reliability of any document is enhanced if it can be shown that the writing occurred soon after the events that the document describes.

• About five thousand early Greek manuscripts of the New Testament have survived, and two of the best preserved go back to around A.D. 350. There are also many manuscript fragments of the New Testament that actually come from the second century A.D., only about a century after Jesus walked the earth. In contrast to this wealth of available manuscripts for the New Testament, a classic such as Caesar's *Gallic War*—which no one would think to question as being completely authentic—is based on only about ten decent manuscripts. Not only that, this particular work was originally written by about 50 B.C., but the earliest manuscript now in existence came along nine hundred years later! There is similarly skimpy manuscript evidence for works like the *History* of Thucydides and the *History* of Herodotus, yet modern historians accept our present texts as trustworthy.

• The reliability of manuscripts can also be established by

finding quotations from them in other works of the time. There are many references and lengthy quotations from Matthew as well as other parts of the New Testament in writings in the latter part of the first century by Clement the bishop of Rome and other church leaders. There are also references to New Testament passages in non-Christian sources of this period—a fact which eliminates any problems that might possibly arise from a pro-Christian bias.

· Scholars have determined that 606 out of the 661 verses of Mark appear in Matthew. This means that even though the complete text of Matthew may have been written later than Mark, a large part of Matthew's Gospel can be regarded as having been committed to writing much earlier—around A.D. 60, the date many experts believe Mark was written.

· Many parts of Matthew, especially those passages containing the sayings of Jesus, are presented in a poetic form, similar to the way that Jewish teachers of the day conveyed words of wisdom to their students. Modern scholars believe that oral history and teaching that are presented in this form are more likely to be preserved accurately for longer periods of time because words uttered in a culturally familiar form are much easier to remember. It's likely, in other words, that Jesus spoke in the known poetic forms of his day when he was teaching and that his listeners were able to commit his teachings to memory until the oral presentation could be placed permanently on paper. In the first part of the second century, Papias, the bishop of Hierapolis in Asia Minor, wrote that Matthew had compiled a "Logia," or collection of Jesus' sayings and teachings. It's quite possible that these poetic sayings came from the mouths of eyewitnesses to Christ's teachings in the Sermon on the Mount and at other familiar New Testament sites.

· Because the contents of Matthew and the other Gospels are based on eyewitness reports, it's unlikely there would be any significant variations from the actual facts as they occurred. In the first place, many Christians would be alive who observed the same sets of events, and they would tend to act as a corrective force on one another. Also, many opponents of Jesus and his first followers would be alive, and if the Gospels were to stand the test of truth with prospective converts, it would be imperative that they be as free of error and as impervious to attack by opponents as possible.

· Archaeological evidence supports the fact that certain Gospel characters and physical locations actually did exist. For example, Pilate's name was recently found on an inscription at the ancient seaport of Caesarea; and the pool of Bethesda—the site of Jesus' healing of the lame man in John 5:2–18—has been extensively excavated in Jerusalem.

· Jesus was definitely accepted as a historical figure by both the Gentile and the Jewish writers of the day. Josephus, the Jewish historian who aided the Romans in their campaign against Jerusalem just before its fall in A.D. 70, refers a number of times to Jesus. Although some of Josephus' statements have been discounted by historians as being later Christian alterations of his original text, it seems quite certain that Josephus did refer to Him as the brother of James; as a person crucified under Pilate; as a reputed miracle worker; as a person who lived at the time the Gospels say He did; as one who claimed to be the Messiah; and as the originator of the Christian faith.

There are several solid reasons, then, why we should regard the New Testament in general—and Matthew's account of the Star of Bethlehem in particular—as a reliable account of actual historical events. But if we do accept Matthew 2 as a reliable factual account, what exactly does the Gospel writer say that the Magi saw? The English translation for the object they saw in the skies is the word "star," but that term has a much richer meaning in both Hebrew and Greek tradition than it does in English. So the second major key that will enable us to unlock the mystery of what happened that day long ago in Bethlehem involves a deeper understanding of this exciting Biblical word.

2. *The ancient meanings of the word "star."* The Hebrew word for "star" appears in the Old Testament only
thirty-seven times, but there is a wide variety of meanings associated with it. The meaning usually involves "star" in a
physical or celestial sense. In Deuteronomy 4:19, for example,
the sun, moon and stars are called "all the host of heaven."

The Hebrew word is also used by comparison to stress vast-
ness or large numbers. Check Genesis 15:5, where "stars" is
used by God to stress how numerous Abraham's descendants
will be.

In four passages in the Old Testament, the word refers to
something different from a celestial star. Joseph dreamed, for
example, that "the sun and moon and eleven stars were bow-
ing down to me." (Genesis 37:9 NIV) His interpretation of
the dream equates the eleven stars with his eleven brothers,
and the sun and moon with his parents, Jacob and Rachel. In
another passage—more directly related to our search for the
Star of Bethlehem—the prophet Balaam predicts "a star will
come out of Jacob; a scepter will rise out of Israel. . . ."
(Numbers 24:17 NIV) The coming Messiah, in other words, is
directly connected with some sort of star.

The Greek word *aster*, which is used in Matthew 2, also is
rich in meaning. Often in the New Testament it means a single star, as opposed to a constellation. Sometimes the word is
used to refer in one way or another to the physical bodies in
the heavens, as when Paul writes, "There is one glory of the
sun, and another glory of the moon, and another glory of the
stars; for star differs from star in glory." (1 Corinthians 15:41
New American Standard Bible).

But more often, New Testament references to stars have
some apocalyptic interpretation—that is, some reference to the
Last Days, when Christ will return to earth. Two instances of
this use in the Gospels are Matthew 24:29 and Mark 13:25,
which refer to the darkening of the sun, moon and stars at the
end of the tribulation, or the period of hardships and troubles
on earth just prior to the Second Coming of Christ.

Most of these apocalyptic uses of "star" occur in the Book of Revelation, and sometimes the word refers to Satan or demons or fallen angels. One probable reference to Satan is Revelation 9:1 (NIV), where John writes, "And the fifth angel sounded his trumpet, and I saw a star that had fallen from the sky to the earth. The star was given the key to the shaft of the Abyss"—the "Abyss" apparently being hell.

It should be evident by now that, as we move into a deeper investigation of the Star of Bethlehem, we have a considerable amount of freedom in deciding exactly what the word "star" means. The Bible has used the word to describe literal celestial bodies, meteors, angels, Christ, Satan, the tribes of Israel and demons.

But does the Star of Bethlehem refer to one of these things or individuals, or was it something completely different? In moving toward an answer to this question, we know now that we have two important keys to unlock the ancient mysteries—the key of a reliable historical record, and the key of understanding the historic breadth of the word "star." Before we go ahead with our search for the Star, however, let's pull together all the threads of information we've gathered so far into one coherent scenario.

CHAPTER FIVE

THE STAR SCENARIO

Our search for the Star up to this point suggests the following sequence of historical events:

Some time between 7 B.C. and the spring of 4 B.C. three or more travelers appeared on the horizon just outside Jerusalem. They had a few attendants with them, but there was nothing particularly striking or memorable about their approach to the city.

As they drew nearer the city walls, it became obvious that they were foreigners because they wore the costumes, including the pointed hats, of Persian holy men and intellectuals. Since Jerusalem was such a cosmopolitan city, with strangers from many parts of the world stopping over for trade or just a short rest on a long journey, some of the merchants who first spotted this small band of wayfarers may have immediately pegged them as members of the priestly Magi tribe. But probably there would have been little reaction among the onlookers other than mild curiosity. In fact, the Jerusalem merchants may well have turned away in disappointment because they knew they weren't going to get much business or practical commercial news from abroad out of these other-worldly fellows!

The Magi, for their part, may have been disappointed for an entirely different reason. As they began to ask around about a star or light they had been observing in the sky but which had recently disappeared, they found nobody even knew anything about it. Apparently, these merchants and other city dwellers had their attention so buried in the mundane things of life that they weren't even aware that something spectacular was being signalled in the skies.

Not only that, the wise men got only blank stares or shakes of the head when they asked about a newborn King of the Jews. The usual reaction was simply, "I really don't know what you're talking about, mister."

Frustrated and puzzled, the Persians might have taken a break from their investigations—and at about the same time they got the fright of their lives. Crazy, evil King Herod wanted to see them immediately. They knew him by reputation, and they didn't like what they had heard. He would as soon kill them as look at them, from all reports, so the Magi may have first considered packing up their things and slipping out of the city as fast as they could.

But they undoubtedly realized they were deep in the heart of Herod's kingdom, and if they were unsuccessful in their attempt to get away, there was little doubt how unpleasant their fate would be. So they took the only logical course open to them: they put on as brave a front as possible and obeyed Herod's summons to the letter.

You can imagine their relief when they entered his palace, walked into his presence and found that he just wanted to discuss the star they had seen and the possibility of the birth of the Messiah. They probably explained to him that they had been trained in astrology, Zoroastrianism and other Persian and Middle Eastern lines of knowledge. Also, they might have stressed that they, like the Jews, were looking for a Savior—or "Sosiosh," as they called the coming Messiah.

But Herod wasn't particularly interested in any discussion of comparative religions. He wanted to get right to the nitty-gritty: What exactly had they seen and how about pooling their knowledge with his in a joint effort to find the Messiah?

The sigh of relief from the Magi must have been heard all over Jerusalem. Herod didn't want to kill them; he actually wanted to help them in their search. So they told him they had seen this light in the sky, a strange light that had disappeared after they realized it was guiding them to Jerusalem. Inexplicably, neither Herod nor his advisers nor anyone else they had encountered in Jerusalem had seen the light, but they knew *they* had, and they also knew that what they had seen was directly related to all their expectations about the appearance of the Savior.

Herod told them he wanted to worship the Messiah himself, so they should let him know if they found him. And the evil king was so adept at dissembling that the Magi, wise as they were, didn't suspect he actually intended to murder the child. Herod, relying on information from his chief priests and Bible scholars, told the Magi that they should go to Bethlehem to continue their search because that was where the prophets had predicted the Messiah would be born.

So, still not suspecting his real motives, they set out for that small town. At this point, they probably had no inkling that Herod was using them as his unknowing agents to pinpoint the location of the infant, nor any suspicion that he would swoop in like an angel of death to destroy the baby, whom he perceived as a threat to his own power. It would certainly have been quite reasonable for them at least to suspect Herod of some sort of hidden or double motives. And a little thought might have revealed to them that it was logical for Herod to use a small group of inconspicuous foreigners to search out and find the child, rather than employing his own highly visible and feared palace guard.

But remember: the Magi may well have feared for their own lives when they entered Herod's presence, so the sense of relief they felt when he actually seemed ready to help them must have obliterated any suspicions and reservations in their minds.

As the Magi hit the road for the short trip to Bethlehem, the light in the sky mysteriously appeared once more. The Star then "went before them," as Matthew puts it, until it came to rest over the place where the child was living. Then they entered the house and when they saw the child Jesus and his mother, Mary, they fell to the ground and worshiped Him, offering them their gifts of gold, incense and myrrh. They thus became the first known Gentiles to meet and worship the Messiah—an event that would serve as a harbinger for the countless other non-Jews who would kneel before Him during the ensuing centuries.

What does this historical narrative tell us about the Star that the wise men followed?

First of all, we know from our background about the meaning of the word "star" in both the Hebrew and New Testament traditions that the term Matthew used could refer to a wide variety of phenomena. Also, we know that the Magi were well equipped through their training to be able to interpret a variety of natural and supernatural lights that might be placed before their path. They were skillful astronomers; they were versed in astrology; and they were open to divine lights that might herald the Savior of Zoroastrianism in some totally unprecedented way.

Not only that, the Magi were by all accounts good men, who showed themselves completely obedient to God. They were conducting an honest search for eternal truth, and when God warned them in a dream not to return to Herod, they obeyed. They returned to their own land by a route that would help them evade the evil king and his cohorts—despite the fact that it would probably have been safer for them personally to follow Herod's original orders and act as his informants. Indeed, if they had been caught trying to slip out of the country without his permission, their lives would have been worth very little.

So the Star that they saw must have been a clear sign to them from God, not from some evil source. And it must have conveyed to them such a sense of spiritual authority and certainty about its meaning that they felt compelled to follow it.

Even more significant for our own search for the identity of the Star are these three points that emerge clearly from Matthew's narrative:

1. *The Star failed to catch the attention of the general public.* Herod and his advisers didn't see it. The ordinary Jews the Magi encountered in Jerusalem didn't know anything about it. Apparently, this peculiar light in the skies was visible and had conveyed its clear identity and meaning only to the Persian wise men.

2. *The Star tended to disappear and then reappear.* In other words, it wasn't a constant spectacle in the skies. The Magi themselves, who were the only ones to see it, lost sight of the light from time to time.

3. *The Star had a directional or guided "beam" of some sort that enabled the Magi to pinpoint the precise location of the Messiah's house.* Matthew tells us that the light came to rest over Jesus' exact location. What kind of star or other heavenly body could have produced such a limited band of light?

As we move into an investigation of some of the specific theories of the identity of the Star of Bethlehem, remember that any theory, to be valid, must measure up to these three physical tests laid down by Matthew in his historical account. Now, to continue our search for the Star, let's divert our gaze from earthly things and look upward, into the galaxies, meteors, comets and other fireworks of deep space.

PART TWO

WHAT WAS THE STAR?

CHAPTER SIX

FIRE IN THE SKY

A tension has often existed between the natural and supernatural explanations of the Star of Bethlehem.

What on the surface appears to be a cool, scientific inquiry may actually turn out to be nothing more than a thinly veiled façade for completely denying the historical validity of Matthew's account. At the same time, some interpretations that attempt to pass for a deep faith in God's ability to change the natural order of things may actually be just wild imagination run amok.

On the supernatural side, for example, Gregory of Tours, who lived in the sixth century A.D., seriously advocated the theory that the Star had really been an angel who had tumbled from the sky into a well in Bethlehem. It wasn't entirely clear how this angelic being had fallen out of orbit—apparently it wasn't a "fallen angel" in the same sense we think of the term! But in any case, Gregory believed that the angel was still trapped at the bottom of that well and could be seen in his own time if curious passersby looked hard enough.[1]

Stories also sprang up that the Star had served as a sort of sparkling, supernatural picture frame for portraits of various members of the Holy Family. Some groups in the Eastern Christian churches thought that the Bethlehem light was a special planet God put in the sky with images of Mary and the Christ child in the center. Another tradition had the planet still in the sky, but this time with the infant Jesus holding a cross.[2]

Such notions are enough to give faith a bad name!

But other interpretations, this time in the name of "science," are hardly any truer to the narrative in Matthew. The theologian William Barclay was always quick to give human reason and scientific truth their due—sometimes at the expense of the Biblical text. In his treatise *The Gospel of Matthew*, he assumes that the Star of Bethlehem was a fixed celestial body and then pushes and pulls Matthew's account to make it conform to his "scientific" presuppositions: "We need not think that the star literally moved like a guide across the sky," Barclay argues. "There is poetry here, and we must not turn lovely poetry into crude and lifeless prose."[3]

In a similar vein, an earlier, nineteenth-century theological writer, Joseph Alexander, said, "It is not said, nor intended, that the star pointed out the house, which is not even mentioned, and which no doubt was ascertained, as in all such cases, by inquiry."[4]

The problem with Barclay and Alexander is that they are so obsessed with the idea of being "scientific" that they've become highly unscientific. Any true scientist would approach the problem of the Star with a blank mind. He would try, as much as possible, to rid himself of all preconceptions and then let the evidence speak for itself. A significant part of the evidence is the historically reliable account in the second chapter of Matthew, and Barclay and Alexander chose to ignore it.

By no stretch of the imagination, for example, can Matthew's narrative be regarded as poetry. As poetry—one wag has said—this part of the first Gospel would make a great newspaper story. The account of the Star is clearly history or perhaps first-century journalism, but not poetry. The passage does *not* say that only the Magi moved while the Star remained stationary. On the contrary, the Star moved too: it "went on before them until it came and stood over where the Child was."

The only way the movement of the Star and its light can be ignored or discounted is either to distort Matthew's lucid, simple description or toss out his account altogether. But this is not the way to get at the truth. In our search for the Star we have to consider all the available evidence as we try to match up the historical accounts with possible happenings in the heavens. So, keeping Matthew's narrative in mind, let's first take a look at one of the most spectacular possibilities for the Star—a "fire in the sky" that could have been created by a meteor, a meteor shower or a bolide.

Meteors, or "falling stars," are a common sight for those who live under rural—or at least unpolluted—skies. One family, who used to live in Texas under clear skies on the periphery of a medium-sized city, got into the habit of sitting in their back yard and looking up at the heavens. The sights they saw were certainly more restful and often considerably more exciting than the situation comedies their television set offered.

As they stared upward at the Milky Way and the various constellations, meteors—as bright as many stars—would periodically streak across their line of vision, sometimes in an arc that seemed to span half the heavens. Often, dozens of these meteors would fall into the atmosphere during the course of an hour.

In earlier times, when much less was known about astronomy, people thought most meteors were visible at low altitudes, perhaps as low as the cloud ceilings overhead. And some also assumed that they could move at extremely slow speed. As a result, one theory of the Star of Bethlehem was that it was a meteor that moved slowly before the Magi at cloud level to lead them to Jerusalem and then actually stopped over Jesus' house.

We know now, of course, that meteors are quite different objects from what was earlier supposed.[5] They are called *me-*

teoroids when they're traveling through space, often at speeds between eight and forty-five miles per second. As they enter the earth's atmosphere, they begin to burn and glow and become flaming *meteors* at an average height of about sixty miles above us. Large meteors may actually survive all the way to the surface of our planet, and in that case their physical remains on earth are called *meteorites*.

The "falling stars" that the Texas family was looking at each evening were thus the flaming spots of light caused by the burning of the meteroid as it turned into a meteor upon encountering the friction of the earth's atmosphere many miles into the sky. The bigger or more durable the meteor, the longer it would emit the flaming, glowing vapors for those below to enjoy. At the most, though, this "fire in the sky" would last only a few brief seconds.

A more impressive variation on the single meteor is the meteor shower. Modern astronomers have determined that the source of a meteor shower—a swarm of thousands of meteors entering the earth's atmosphere at the same time—is a comet, or more specifically, the debris of comets. Comets usually follow a certain path through space and at various times they may lose some of their physical matter. This debris continues to move through space in about the same orbit as the comet, but it may finally intersect the path of a planet, and then the gravitational force of the planet will pull the scattering of these comet meteroids into its atmosphere.

This process regularly happens as our earth passes through bunches of orbiting meteroids, and meteor showers are the result. Sometimes, the showers involve only a short burst of meteors. But on other occasions, the shower may be so extensive and cover such a long period of time that observers may actually begin to wonder if perhaps the sky is beginning to fall and the end of the earth is near!

On two such occasions, recorded in 1833 and again in 1866, as many as two hundred thousand meteors could be seen emerging from one point in the sky over a span of several hours.[6] The effect was so dramatic and unexpected that many people on earth who witnessed the events believed that the shower was something put in the heavens by God to foretell the end of the world.[7] Another spectacular meteor shower occurred on October 9, 1933—within the memory of many people still living today. The maximum rate of "falling stars" at that time was several thousand meteors per hour. But the potential for fear and panic among the onlookers had been greatly reduced because, unlike the nineteenth-century situation, scientists had predicted the advent of the shower, so the general population was more prepared.

The most spectacular kind of "fire in the sky" is the bolide, or fireball. The bolide is, in effect, a very large meteor that emits a much larger and more spectacular light than an ordinary single meteor. In fact, some bolides are so huge that they may reach the brilliance of the full moon and are even visible in broad daylight. They leave luminous trails behind them, which may persist for periods ranging from a second to a half hour.

Some scientists believe that bolides were responsible for the huge craters and other massive devastation discovered both in Arizona and in a remote part of Siberia. The Siberian incident, which involved the complete flattening of trees over a huge area, has been likened to some sort of nuclear blast and has even been attributed by some theorists to a violent probe of this planet by alien creatures from outer space. But more cautious scientific minds suggest that the more probable cause of the destruction is a bolide.

These descriptions of meteors, meteor showers and bolides should immediately suggest some similarities to and differences from the Star of Bethlehem. First of all, the startling impact of a bolide or meteor shower would have made anyone sit up and take notice. And any of these three astronomical happenings would have lighted the sky for a brief period and then disappeared—much as the Star is supposed to have provided intermittent guidance for the Magi.

A particularly attractive explanation is that the Star may actually have consisted of a combination of things—perhaps a meteor shower and a meteor, or a bolide and a meteor shower. There may even have been a conjunction of stars that had some astrological significance, and then a bolide or meteor shower may have occurred nearby to enhance the importance of the event.

But there are many more problems with these interpretations than there are convincing arguments in favor of connecting them to the identity of the Star. First of all, the Magi would probably not have recognized the appearance of a meteor shower or bolide—even a rather impressive one—as heralding the birth of a great king. There's simply no indication in ancient literature that any of these "fires in the sky"—no matter how impressive the cosmological fireworks—would have been seen as the harbinger of the Messiah.

Also, the very spectacular nature of the meteor shower and bolide is an argument against them. One of the requirements of the Star of Bethlehem, as we've seen from the account in Matthew, is that it may have been impressive to the Magi, but apparently nobody else in the vicinity witnessed it. A meteor shower would surely have been noticed in Jerusalem and the surrounding towns because it would have "exploded," or radiated from such a high point in the earth's atmosphere. And even a bright fireball, or bolide, even though its light would have been more localized, could have been seen—and most likely would have been seen by someone who would have made a report to Herod—in a one-hundred-fifty-mile radius.

But neither Herod nor his chief priests and scribes were aware of the Star that the wise men had witnessed, so another serious objection must be made against these fires in the sky.

Finally, there seems to be no way that a meteor shower or bolide—and surely not an ordinary, single meteor—could have "stood over" the house where the child was and indicated Jesus' location to the Magi. It may be that some quirk of lighting or shadows from a bright light like a bolide could have made one house stand out over another. But it seems unlikely that such a marginal indication of the Messiah would have been enough to convince the wise men.

So, as spectacular and riveting as a bolide or a meteor shower or even a single sustained meteor may be, they each fall short of the historical tests that could qualify them as the Star of Bethlehem. But these are only the first in a number of possibilities for the Star. Let's turn our attention now to another set of theories—those that focus on the Bethlehem light as coming from only one, fixed heavenly body.

CHAPTER SEVEN

ONE HEAVENLY BODY?

Because the word that the wise men used to describe the Star of Bethlehem—the Greek word *aster*—usually refers to a single luminous body in the sky, many have focused their efforts on searching for only one heavenly body.

Some have built theories around an eclipse of the sun or moon. Others have concluded that the Star was actually a bright, twinkling star. And still others have chosen some prominent planet as the most likely candidate. There are a number of good arguments for following this one-heavenly-body approach. In fact, proving any contrary theory will probably result in many disappointed traditionalists who have always loved the postcard pictures of the single glowing star over the three wise men.

But just how strong are the arguments for one of those well-known heavenly bodies that still light up our night skies?

The eclipse theory can be disposed of rather quickly. Both solar and lunar eclipses were regarded by the ancients as portents of some impending evil event. The birth of the Messiah, or the Persian Sosiosh, or the good king that the Magi were expecting was by nature a good event. So the fundamental sign or inner meaning conveyed by the eclipse would be the exact opposite of what the Magi would have been led to anticipate.

Also, solar eclipses are quite rare for any given part of the earth. And the only times the moon passed between the sun and the earth—and thus blocked out the sun's light and caused an eclipse over Persia anywhere near the time of Christ—were in 10 B.C. and in A.D. 29.[1] Neither of these dates fit in to our required time frame of roughly 8–4 B.C. for the appearance of the Star.

Finally, despite the latitude the ancients had in employing the word "star," it's unlikely that term would be attached to an eclipse of the sun or the moon. A star, after all, is a body that emits light, while an eclipse involves the blocking out of light. It's hard to see how any kind of eclipse could measure up to the qualities required of the Star.

But what about the possibility that the Star of Bethlehem may actually have been a star in the sense we use the word today?

One idea that has attracted some supporters is that the so-called dog star, Sirius, which is located in the constellation Canis Major (Big Dog) and is the brightest star in the heavens, might have been the Star described by Matthew. Sirius is bright, by the way, not because it gives off more light than other stars but because it's so close to earth—less than nine light-years, or about 51 million million miles away.

It seems there is some evidence that between 5 and 2 B.C. Sirius rose "heliacally"—or at sunrise—on the first day of the Egyptian month Mesori and shone with exceptional brightness. The theologian William Barclay has argued that since *Mesori* means "the birth of a prince," ancient astrologers would have interpreted this appearance of Sirius as announcing the birth of a great king.[2]

The problem with this view is that the astronomers and astrologers of Christ's day were quite familiar with all the movements of Sirius, and they wouldn't have been particularly impressed by its heliacal rising because this occurred frequently in the skies. Also, it seems somewhat artificial to pick out the name of an *Egyptian* month and try to make a case for this to have an important meaning for Persian wise men traveling in Judea. The relationship between these facts is just a little too tenuous to cause sophisticated intellectuals like the Magi to sit up and take notice.

As far as Sirius or another star is concerned, we also have to keep in mind the basic features of the Star of Bethlehem: Herod and his advisers could have seen Sirius as easily as the Magi; and also there's no indication that this star appeared and disappeared in the way the Star of Bethlehem did.

Another candidate is the star Spica, which also is quite bright and tends to appear off by itself. The isolated nature of Spica's appearances is reflected in its Arabic name, *Al Azal*, which means "the separate one." One scholar has calculated that Spica rose heliacally, or on the eastern horizon just before sunrise, with unusual brightness and distinction in 1 B.C.[3] But the date immediately rules this star out because, as we've seen, Herod died in 4 B.C., and the Star of Bethlehem had to appear prior to his death.

In addition to the dating problem, the same objections against Sirius also apply to Spica. In other words, Spica is a normal, predictable, fixed star which would have aroused little interest among the Magi and which apparently could not shine its light in the highly localized way described in Matthew 2:9.

But if an actual star won't measure up to the Star of Bethlehem's standards, what about a planet?

Several planets, including Mercury, Venus, Jupiter, Saturn and Mars, have been placed in the running for the designation as the renowned "star in the east." Mercury, for example, can be seen on several consecutive days shining brightly for a short period, low in the eastern sky. The problem, though, is similar to the problems we've considered with the stars Sirius and Spica. Mercury's movements were regular and predictable and thus would have caused little extraordinary interest among ancient astronomers. Also, Mercury couldn't have moved to guide the Magi as the Star in Matthew's Gospel did.

Venus has always been a more popular candidate for the Star for a number of reasons. In the first place, Venus is the brightest object in the heavens, apart from the sun and the moon. It easily outshines even the brightest star, Sirius, and has occupied an important position in astronomy and astrology since ancient times.

Venus has often been called the morning star because it can be seen clearly when it rises in the morning just before the sun comes up. Biblical writers, acutely aware of the prominence of Venus, have drawn parallels between this bright planet and Christ Himself. John, writing in Revelation 22:16, reports Jesus as saying, "I am the Root and the Offspring of David, the bright Morning Star." (NIV)

Long before Christ was born, ancient observers of the heavens saw astrological and mythical significance in Venus. As a matter of fact, some of the earliest astronomical references, estimated to have been written around 1800 B.C. on the so-called Venus tablets of Ammizadura, go into some detail about the significance of Venus.[4] But how could Venus have guided the Magi or pointed out Jesus' house?

There are advocates for a few other planets as well. It's been suggested that Jupiter, the largest planet in our solar system, may have been the Star because it was known in ancient times as "the king's star." In other words, some heavenly event relating to Jupiter might herald the birth or death of an earthly king. Saturn has also been offered as a possibility because there was supposed to be some connection between Saturn and the nation of Israel. The Roman historian Tacitus mentions a tradition that associates the Jews with the planet Saturn.

The major problem with both Jupiter and Saturn, though, is that, by themselves, they don't seem bright or unusual enough to have prompted Persian Magi to have traveled a great distance to search for a Savior at the time that Christ was an infant.

One of the most interesting theories that favors a planet—and one of the most convincingly marshaled arguments—focuses on Mars. Mars at various times of the year sheds a bright reddish glow that rivals the luminosity of the brightest planets. The Reverend David Fotheringham, a British cleric, wrote a book more than a half century ago advocating Mars as the Star, and his presentation is one of the strongest for this planet.[5] Here's the main thrust of it:

In ancient times, the heliacal rising and setting of stars and planets—or their rising in the east just before the sun comes up—was the subject of much more attention than it is now. The destinies of individual people were thought to be closely tied in to the movement of the heavenly bodies, so even the average man on the street knew something about heliacal risings. Each planet would move around the heavens during a fixed period of weeks, months or years and would always go back behind the sun, only to be "reborn" or to rise again and begin a new period of movement.

So when the Magi said, "We have seen his star in the east," they must have been referring to one of these heliacal risings, according to Fotheringham. But the question is, What star or planet did they see?

Our British scholar cites the Alexandrian mathematician and astronomer Ptolemy, who lived during the second century A.D., as authority for the idea that all the ancient countries had been assigned certain planets as their main source of heavenly influence. And the planet associated with the destiny of Judea was Mars.

Fotheringham finds further support for Mars as the Star of Bethlehem when he delves into the Gospel of Matthew. In particular, he notes that in Matthew 2:16, Herod ordered all boys in Bethlehem and its vicinity who were *two years old and under* to be killed. But why two years of age?

Some have speculated that Herod somehow knew that the

purported Messiah might be as old as two years and he therefore wanted to wipe out any youngster who might fall into
that age range. But Fotheringham sees a connection between
Herod's order and the amount of time it takes for Mars to
make one complete loop around the skies. You see, Mars is
the only star or planet whose period is two years. In contrast,
the time it takes the fixed stars to make one trip around the
heavens is one year. And the planets vary from eighty-eight
days for Mercury to many years for the more distant planets.
But Mars takes two years—the exact figure Herod seized upon
in his order to kill the children in Bethlehem.

In other words, the argument goes, Herod discovered from
the Magi that they had been following Mars since its recent
heliacal rising—and that must have occurred no more than
about two years prior to the time they were meeting with him
in his palace. As a result, Herod reasoned, if the wise men had
really received some correct divine message from Mars about
the birth of a "King of the Jews," the infant must have been
less than two years old. So just to be safe, Herod killed all the
boys in the relevant age range in Bethlehem and the surrounding countryside.

This is a fascinating theory, but there are a number of problems that critics have noted. The biggest problem is that in
order to fit in the known heliacal risings of Mars around the
time of Christ's birth, it's necessary to place the nativity in 3
B.C. instead of 4 B.C. Fotheringham does this by an ingenious
counting theory that allows Herod to reign an extra year and
die in 3 B.C. instead of 4 B.C. Unfortunately, this view isn't
generally accepted by historians who have studied that era.

The other difficulties with the Mars theory center on those
that have made us question the other star and planetary interpretations: How would Mars have directed a beam of light so
that the Magi could have been guided quite clearly to Jesus'
house? Also, why wouldn't Mars have been seen and understood by Herod's advisers, who were themselves quite knowl-

edgeable about the movements and meanings of the heavenly bodies?

A major objection against these star and planetary theories is that the ordinary stars and planets in our heavens lack the ability to emit a directional light or beam. But there have continually been attempts to answer this objection, and one of the most ingenious goes far back into early Christian tradition.

It's quite possible that the Magi may have made it to Jerusalem by "following" a particular star or planet, such as Mars, that had some association with Judea. And then they would have made it to Bethlehem by following Herod's instructions that Hebrew prophecies identified that little town six miles from Jerusalem as the birthplace of the Messiah. But how would they have known which house Jesus resided in? A star or planet standing directly over Jerusalem would also have seemed to be standing directly over Bethlehem and every home in Bethlehem. It would have taken highly sophisticated astronomical instruments, which were not available to the Magi, to determine whether a particular star or planet was directly over Jerusalem as opposed to Bethlehem—much less to distinguish between different houses in Bethlehem.

But somewhere back in the mists of the distant past, a tradition arose that the star the Magi had been following guided them to the specific house in Bethlehem in this manner: It seems that the Magi stopped beside a deep well as they came into Bethlehem. The purpose of their stopping, though, wasn't to get a drink of water. Instead, they took another midnight observation of the star by using the well's perpendicular walls as a fixed observatory. By looking down at the reflection of the star in the precise center of the still water, they were able to determine with great accuracy that they were at exactly the place or location where the Child was.[6]

It's true that a similar primitive astronomical method was used at Syene in Egypt to determine the line of the Tropic of Cancer. In that case, the reflection of the sun in a well was the key to the calculations. But as far as the Star of Bethlehem is concerned, that ancient tradition about the well doesn't say how the Magi distinguished between the various houses—perhaps the well they stopped at was supposed to be the very well attached to Jesus' home. In any case, it's a compelling old tradition and may convince some readers, but there are other theories about the Star that are at least as convincing.

Before we move on to those other explanations, though, let's take a few moments to consider an important cultural difference between our own times and the situation that existed at the birth of Christ. We've spent a great deal of time talking about such notions as "heliacal risings" of various planets and the deeper significance of stars and planets for the destinies of men and nations. All this may sound like Greek to you—and it was indeed a matter of Greek and Latin and Persian and Arabic tradition. For the peoples who lived at the time Christ was born were deeply enmeshed in world views that took the heavens much more seriously than we do today.

If you stop the average man or woman on the street and start questioning him about the objects in the skies above them, he would know something about the sun and the moon and he surely could point those two bodies out to you. Also, he would have heard something about Mars and Venus, and Jupiter, perhaps because those planets have been in the news as a result of recent space probes.

But it's doubtful that more than a handful of people could point out any of these planets, and most people can't get beyond the Big Dipper (if they get that far!) in making observations about stars and constellations. What all this means is that our culture has a very casual attitude toward the heavens. We know little and care less—unless NASA decides to put an astronaut up there or some faraway spaceship is sending back spectacular close-ups of Saturn and its rings.

The people of Jesus' day had exactly the opposite attitude. The highly educated Magi were very much aware of movements in the heavens—but so was the man on the street. If you could travel back in time, after taking a quick course in Aramaic, which was the common language of ancient Palestine, and then do a few man-on-the-street interviews in Jerusalem in 4 B.C., you'd be amazed at what you'd hear about heliacal risings of Mars and the spiritual significance of Jupiter and Venus.

A recognition of how different our attitude toward the heavens is from that of the people of Jesus' day is essential if you're going to grasp the full significance of the next section of this book—the all-important astrological attempts to explain the Star of Bethlehem.

CHAPTER EIGHT

A GATHERING
OF STARS:
ASTROLOGICAL
INTERPRETATIONS

We live in an age when horoscopes, divination of the stars and planets and other astrological practices have gained new popularity.

Certainly, most people these days don't come close to the ordinary people of Christ's time in knowledge of the heavens. But there is a similar desire to impose order and predictability on the seeming chaos of our lives. And astrology is vying for a place with traditional religious faith in the ultimate spiritual commitments of contemporary men and women.

We should recognize at the outset of any discussion of possible astrological elements in the Star of Bethlehem that both the Old and the New Testaments take a negative view of astrology. One of the earliest references to false divination, which is usually taken to include astrology, is Deuteronomy 18:12. This passage concludes, "For whoever does these things is detestable to the Lord; and because of these detesta-

ble things the Lord your God will drive them out before you."
(NASB)

There are also some other rather hard words reserved
specifically for astrology:

· God told Babylon, "You are wearied with your many
counsels, let now the astrologers, those who prophesy by the
stars, those who predict by the new moons, stand up and save
you from what will come upon you." (Isaiah 47:13 NASB)

· The prophet Jeremiah warned Israel: "Do not learn the
way of the nations, and do not be terrified by the signs of the
heavens although the nations are terrified by them." (Jeremiah 10:2 NASB)

· God called down judgment on Israel for worshiping Saturn (or Kiyyun) in Amos 5:25-26.

· The Old Testament also says that Israel fell and was
conquered by surrounding nations because of involvement in
pagan worship, including showing homage to "all the host of
heaven." (See 2 Kings 17:16-18; 21:2, 5-6.)

The official position of the Jewish religious leaders at the
time of Christ would have been opposed to any linking of astrology with the coming of the Messiah. But at the same time,
there was a strong sense that God was in control of the
heavens. There seems no reason to assume that there would
have been any opposition among the Jewish priests to having
the heavens, in some way, declare such a momentous event as
the coming of the long awaited Savior.

Also, even though a pure and uncompromising relationship
with God prohibited any consorting with divination or astrology, the Hebrew people had always had a tradition of stray-
ing from the straight and narrow path. The Old Testament is
replete with references to the ordinary people wandering off
into worship of "sacred pillars" or "hill shrines" or "baals"—
the host of pagan fertility gods and other false deities of the
earth and fields. So it's likely that at the time of Christ there

was a spiritual underground of deviant superstitions, including astrology. This idea is not so hard to grasp when you consider that perfectly intelligent people in our own day are drawn to horoscopes and "predictions" of the future by supposed seers like Jeane Dixon, who turn out to be wrong on many occasions.

You may object, however, "If God was so opposed to astrology and divination, why would He have allowed it to be a key factor in leading the wise men to Jesus?"

That's a good question, and it deserves a serious, complete answer. It's true, as we've seen, that God and His prophets always condemned the use of astrology. But it's also true that He wanted to announce the birth of His Son to Gentiles who didn't acknowledge or perhaps even have a very clear understanding of the Hebrew Scriptures. To get the point about the Messiah across to them, it was necessary to communicate in their own idiom—and that may well have included their understanding of astrology.[1]

Of course, this is not to say that God approved of astrology, even if He may have used it to speak to the Magi. There are many other examples of God's using practices or rituals He disapproved of to communicate His message. Balaam, in the Book of Numbers, was involved in pagan divination and oracles, but one of the most important star prophecies in the Old Testament came through him. You'll recall that passage we've quoted often in this book, from Numbers 24:17: ". . . a star will come out of Jacob, a scepter will rise out of Israel. . . ." (NIV)

Other examples of God's turning bad practices or situations around to get His message across include Joseph's being sold into slavery by his brothers. This evil became the channel by which he eventually became a ruler in Egypt and the savior of his family. Also, you may recall that Jeremiah predicted that Nebuchadnezzar, ruler of Babylonia, would be used by God to punish Egypt, and that's exactly what happened when

Babylonia invaded that nation in the sixth century B.C. (see Jeremiah 46:13ff.).

In none of these cases did God necessarily approve of the channel that was used to bring about His message or His will. But that didn't prevent Him from redirecting the forces of evil to achieve good.

So whether there is any astrological significance to the account of the Star or not, it's still important for us to take astrology into account in our search for the Star of Bethlehem. Otherwise, we may find ourselves ignoring another of those cases when God used an evil or questionable practice to put His will and message into effect.

But was there any astrological significance to the sighting of the Star of Bethlehem by the Magi? If astrology did enter in here, then it would seem quite likely that the Star had something to do with the movement of known stars or planets. So if we're going to explore adequately every possible interpretation of the Star, it's necessary for us to spend some time with various astrological interpretations in order to get at the truth.

Let's acknowledge at the outset that there are a couple of elements in the account of the Star in the second chapter of Matthew that tend to support the notion that astrology was involved in some way. First of all, the Magi, as we've seen, would have had some knowledge of astrology—whether they were Persian priests, Babylonian diviners, or whatever. And secondly, when they say in Matthew 2:2 (NIV), "We saw *his* star in the east," they seem to be referring to a heavenly light specifically associated with the Messiah. In determining horoscopes, astrologers always point to some key planet or star as being the main heavenly body in determining the destiny of an individual.

But these apparent connections with astrological practice don't in themselves decide the case. Before we come to any final conclusions on this issue, let's take a closer look at the way astrology had developed up to the time of Christ.

Religion and scientific investigation were closely linked in early historic and prehistoric times, and both astrology and rudimentary forms of astronomy arose and existed side by side. The intellectuals of those early days studied the movements of the heavens quite closely, and they came to inject their own religious ideas into the scientific observations they were making.

The ancient Babylonians in the Mesopotamian Valley in the Middle East were among the most sophisticated in studying the heavens—and also in developing the spiritual side of their discipline, astrology. The Chaldean (or Babylonian) priests of those days believed that if they could understand the details of the heavenly movements, they could predict the future and thus, to some extent, control their own destinies.

At this stage, though, astrology focused primarily on the destiny of nations or the meaning of the most earth-shaking events—not on the destinies of ordinary individuals. It took the Medes, or Persians, who conquered the Babylonians, to extend the idea of astrology from the global to the personal.[2] The Persians were the first to cast individual horoscopes, and toward the last days of their empire, they came up with the idea for the twelve signs of the zodiac. The zodiac is a theoretical band 16 to 18 degrees wide that sweeps through the skies, from one horizon to the other. It moves through the paths of each of the planets and is divided into twelve equal "signs," each 30 degrees in length.

Each of these twelve segments of the sky also contains a constellation which was given a specific name that came to be associated with a sign of the zodiac. These twelve signs, or constellation names, are Aries, Taurus, Gemini, Cancer, Leo, Virgo, Libra, Scorpio, Sagittarius, Capricorn, Aquarius and Pisces.

Later conquerors of the Middle East contributed their own peculiar additions to this basic astrological framework. The Greeks, for example, who conquered the Persians in the fourth century B.C., put the twelve signs into four groups to represent the four elements of Greek pantheism—earth, air,

fire and water. And the Egyptians, just before the birth of
Christ, subdivided each of the 30-degree "signs," or segments
in the heavens, into three "decans," or 10-degree measure-
ments.

If all this sounds rather complicated and even confusing or
silly, remember you're viewing things from a twentieth-cen-
tury perspective. These people were reaching out for some
sort of spiritual truth—just as astrology buffs of our own day
are doing—but they had rather limited spiritual resources.

And just so you won't assume this kind of thinking is limited to the time of Christ and earlier, consider a more recent
attempt to fit the Star of Bethlehem account into an astrological mold:

In an article that came out in *Popular Astronomy* in 1918,[3]
the writer Stansbury Hagar draws a parallel between Matthew's account and stories about virgin mothers and their
divine children in pagan cults. Specifically, he mentions a festival of a virgin mother and divine child celebrated at Alex-
andria at midnight on December 25 for several centuries before and after the birth of Christ. He also brings in the Hindu
deity Krishna, who he says was born in the presence of shepherds, and Gautama Siddhartha Buddha, whose birth was
marked by the appearance of a supernatural light.

Then he gets down to his main point: In his view, the account of the Star of Bethlehem is nothing more than a poetic
and symbolic description by Hebrew priests of what was
going on in the heavens on the night of December 22—the
winter solstice. At the winter solstice, the shortest day of the
year, as many psychologists will tell you, strange things tend to
happen. People get depressed by the cold and the dark, and
emotional crises and even suicides start to climb. You may
have experienced some of these negative feelings yourself
when the warmth of spring seems so far away.

To counter this depressing time of the year, different cultures have developed festivals to keep people's spirits up, and
Hagar sees the Star account in Matthew as directly related to

this solstice phenomenon. He argues that the Star of Bethlehem was nothing more than a group of stars or a constellation that signaled at a certain time to ancient astronomers the approach of the depressing winter solstice.

The scenario he paints is really quite ingenious—even if it has little connection with the historical narrative in Matthew. Hagar imagines the Jewish priests standing under a clear night sky, watching the movement of the constellation Aries, the "Ram," across the heavens as a sort of celestial announcement of the new year's sun. Then other stars, representing the Magi, come into view, and finally the bright star Spica rises at midnight to introduce the "Virgin," or the constellation Virgo. The entire Star of Bethlehem scene, in other words, is played out overhead in the heavens, rather than among real people on earth in Judea!

Such a theory may provoke some mild interest among historians and philosophers who specialize in ancient myths. But it's of little use to us in our search for the real Star. We're committed to stick to the facts, and that means we have to take Matthew's description seriously—not as the starting point for some fanciful speculations that have no basis in reality.

While an approach like Hagar's may be unattractive, there are other astrological theories that are more worthy of our consideration. In particular, early astrologers and astronomers were quite interested in the meaning of the conjunction—or coming together—of certain stars and planets. And some of the conjunction theories of the Star of Bethlehem have gained an extremely wide number of supporters.

There's good reason for the high popularity of the conjunction view of the Star: it's scientifically respectable. Astronomers have made accurate determinations that planetary conjunctions actually did occur in 7 and 6 B.C. Also, these "gatherings of the stars" were sufficiently unusual to carry great significance for astrologers and astronomers of Christ's day.

The German astronomer Johannes Kepler was the first to

put forward this theory back in the early seventeenth century. Although he had calculated that a conjunction of Jupiter and Saturn would occur on December 17, 1603, both planets were so near the sun in the morning sky that he couldn't see Saturn. But about a week later, on December 25, he did see Jupiter, Saturn and Mercury forming a small triangle in the sky.[4]

Kepler kept track of the movements of Jupiter and Saturn during the ensuing months, and he noticed that these two tended to separate and then draw together again while Mars moved closer and closer to them. Finally, in late September of 1604, Saturn, Jupiter and Mars came together in a tight triangle and, as though on cue, a supernova—or light from the explosion of some faraway star—appeared suddenly near the triangle and finally faded completely from sight in March 1606.

The spectacular quality of the supernova, combined with the planetary triangle, prompted Kepler to speculate whether some similar heavenly event might have been the Star of Bethlehem. He threw himself more diligently into his research and came up with these findings:

First of all, a "triple conjunction" of Jupiter and Saturn had occurred in the sign of Pisces, or the "Fish," in 7 B.C. This means that Jupiter, moving west to east, first caught up to Saturn in the sky and then passed it to form the first conjunction. Then, from the viewpoint of observers on earth, Jupiter seemed to stop moving away from Saturn and actually began to back up in the sky in an east-to-west movement until the two planets came together again. This passing constituted the second conjunction. Finally, Jupiter changed direction once more, resuming its west-to-east motion, and passed Saturn for the third time to form the third conjunction.

The backward, or retrograde, motion of Jupiter puzzled observers before it was explained in the sixteenth century in relation to the earth's motion around the sun. Ancient astronomers and astrologers thought the backward and forward movements reflected the motion of the gods who moved about the skies as they were led by their whims.

Later research has confirmed Kepler's finding that a triple conjunction of Jupiter and Saturn did indeed occur in 7 B.C., though there is some disagreement as to the exact dates on which it occurred. The most accepted modern calculation is that the conjunctions came about on May 29, September 29 and December 4. In any case, it was a rare enough occurrence to have caused astrologers of the day to take notice. Triple conjunctions of this type only occur on an average of once every 125 years, while single conjunctions between two planets take place more frequently.

Taking this much of Kepler's research, some Star theoreticians have concluded the Magi were involved in this sequence of events: The first conjunction of Saturn and Jupiter started them on their journey from Persia to Jerusalem because the planet Jupiter was associated with the birth of kings and Saturn was supposed to have some impact on the destiny of Judea. Also, the conjunction took place in the Pisces constellation, which, as we've seen, was associated in the minds of ancient stargazers with the Jews.

The second conjunction would have happened during their journey to hasten them on the way. And the last one would have occurred as they left Herod in Jerusalem and headed toward Bethlehem. The Star, in other words, was three strategically placed conjunctions of Jupiter and Saturn in the appropriate constellation.

Those who favor this triple-conjunction theory bolster their argument by citing an old rabbinic tradition that says that the births of Abraham and Moses were also accompanied by conjunctions.

But there are also a number of problems with this explanation of the Star. In the first place, no ancient writer proposed this theory that the Jupiter-Saturn triple conjunction in the Pisces constellation heralded the birth of the Messiah in Judea. All the theories come from much later writers who have picked up the astrological threads of the distant past and then tried to weave them together.

Also, it's been shown that the two planets never came closer to each other than about one degree, or double the diameter of the full moon. In other words, the conjunction would have carried only astrological significance and wouldn't have been at all impressive to the ordinary eye. Some conjunctions can actually make planets look like one star, but that wasn't the case with those that occurred in 7 B.C. A much closer conjunction of Saturn and Jupiter took place in 66 B.C., only 59 years earlier, and so it's natural to ask why this more dramatic joining of planets didn't prompt other Magi to set out toward Jerusalem.[5]

But this is not the end of the conjunction theories. For Johannes Kepler, back there in the seventeenth century, came up with some other interesting findings. He discovered not only the triple conjunction of 7 B.C. but also a conjunction of three planets—Saturn, Mars and Jupiter—in 6 B.C. It seems that first, in February of that year, Mars passed Saturn and then the next month, in March, Mars passed Jupiter. Mars, you'll recall, was also thought by the ancients to have some connection with Judea. There's some dispute as to whether this planetary grouping may have been too near the sun in the low western sky to be seen with the naked eye. But if a triangle of Mars, Saturn and Jupiter could have been seen then, some interesting possibilities arise concerning the Star of Bethlehem.

Some writers have speculated that the Star may have been a combination of the triple conjunction of 7 B.C. and the three-planet conjunction of 6 B.C. Others say it may have involved one or both of these heavenly happenings, along with a comet or nova in the midst of them. We'll devote some time later on to the significance of comets, novas and supernovas, but for the moment, let's consider in greater detail one of the best-argued combination-of-conjunctions theories.

The chain of events would go like this: First, the Magi would get started after seeing the first Jupiter-Saturn conjunction in Pisces on May 27, 7 B.C. Then the next Jupiter-Saturn conjunction would occur on October 5 of that year, slightly farther to the west. Thus, the wise men would know they were heading in the right direction: They would in effect be "following the star."

The third Jupiter-Saturn conjunction would occur even farther to the west on December 1, 7 B.C., and the Magi would continue to "follow the star" to Jerusalem. The triangular grouping of Saturn and Jupiter with Mars on February 25 might have encouraged them on their way because it occurred even farther to the west than the third Jupiter-Saturn conjunction.

Finally, two conjunctions occurred later in 6 B.C.—one with Venus and Saturn on April 24 and another with Venus and Jupiter on May 8. This final grouping would have been clearly visible in the morning sky and would have pointed generally from Jerusalem in the direction of Bethlehem.

It's possible, in other words, that Magi steeped in astrological lore might have seen sufficient significance in each of these conjunctions to "follow" them as they occurred in a westerly direction across the sky toward Judea. The fact that the planets and constellations were intimately associated with the destiny of Judea would have further confirmed the direction they were pointing in the skies.

But there are many problems with these astrological interpretations of the Star. First of all, there were a number of other significant conjunctions that occurred during this general period, but for some reason they didn't get the attention of the Magi. Also, nobody really knows for certain the meaning of *any* of these conjunctions. Again, we're building theories as modern scholars looking back on a time almost two thousand years in the past, but we really don't have enough information about specific astrological views in that era to build an airtight case for the Star's identity. Words have to be placed into the Magi's mouths and thoughts have to be injected into their minds—words and thoughts which more than likely weren't there at all.

But one of the most telling objections to the conjunction

theories is the fact that the word Matthew uses for star—*aster* —generally means a *single* luminous body. Other words were normally employed to indicate a grouping of planets or stars, such as a conjunction or constellation.

Everything in Matthew's narrative points toward one bright body of some sort; yet we've seen that none of these conjunctions came close enough together to be regarded as one "star" by any stretch of the imagination.

Finally, even if we grant that the Magi followed these conjunctions to Jerusalem and then headed toward Bethlehem as the conjunctions involving Venus pointed in that direction, we're left with the same questions posed earlier in this book: Why didn't Herod or any of his advisers know of the significance of any of these conjunctions—after all, the planets were right up there for all to see, weren't they? Also, once the Magi got to Bethlehem by "following" the Venus conjunctions, how did they find the particular house where Jesus was living? Every time the Magi moved in Bethlehem, the conjunction would seem to be over a different house—unless some directional light were being beamed down, and none of these conjunction theories provides adequately for this.

So despite the fact that the Magi were probably well equipped to interpret astrological signs, it's obvious that there are many holes in the astrological approach to the Star. The Star of Bethlehem must have been brighter and more mobile than any of the ordinary heavenly bodies we can see in the sky on a clear night. With this idea in mind, let's turn to some of the more dramatic objects that appear from time to time in the heavens—and in the view of many probably did appear at the time of Christ's birth.

CHAPTER NINE

THE CHINESE "SWEEPING STAR"

Among the most dramatic heavenly events recorded by the ancient Chinese were the periodic *hui hsing,* or "sweeping stars," that blazed a bright trail across the skies, often for a year or more at a time.[1]

Early astronomers were often startled and puzzled about the meaning of these spectacular bodies, which we today call comets. This word, by the way, comes from the Greek word *kometes,* meaning "long-haired"—a reference to the "tails" that give comets their distinctive look.

Because of the striking appearance of comets, it was natural the idea would spring up that perhaps one of them was actually the Star of Bethlehem. Early stargazers associated comets with evil omens, gigantic disasters and revolutions more often than they did with positive happenings. But a tradition arose long ago that a comet could also signal an illustrious birth, or the arrival of a great leader of some sort. Christian writers seized on this possibility because a comet seemed at first glance like such a likely interpretation of the Star.

A Christian writer of the third century, Origen, wrote, "The star that was seen in the east we consider to have been a new star . . . such as comets, or those meteors which resemble beams of wood, or beards or wine jars. We have read . . . that on some occasions also, when good was to happen, comets made their appearance. . . . If then, at the commencement of new dynasties . . . there arises a comet . . . why should it be a matter of wonder that at the birth of Him who was to introduce a new doctrine to the human race . . . a star should have arisen?"[2]

To evaluate this theory that the Star was a comet, it's necessary first to take a close look at exactly what a comet is. A comet consists mainly of swarms of particles and glowing gases that revolve in orbit around the sun. They can be seen even when they are millions of miles distant from the earth, and they rise and set with the stars and planets and may actually seem to be standing still when you first look at them. If you watch them closely, though, from night to night during the weeks or months they are in the sky, you'll see them move gradually across the heavens.

When comets are far away from the sun, they are invisible—nothing like the spectacular, fiery balls when they are visible to us overhead. Composed mainly of frozen gases with some rock and metal mixed in, they have even been described as resembling "large, dirty snowballs." Some experts estimate that the average comet may have only a trillionth of the mass of the earth, so they actually contain a lot of empty space. In fact, one scientist has described a comet as "the nearest thing to nothing that anything can be and still be something."[3]

The reason that the relatively small and airy comets seem so huge to us is that they develop gigantic tails when they approach the sun because of the increasing heat and solar pressure. The comet's tail always points away from the sun and can "grow" so long it can reach out into space as far as 200 million miles. But when comets get very near the sun, even the densest portions—what we call the "head," or the leading part—is still so gauzy that stars can be seen through it.

Now, what about some concrete Star theories involving specific comets?

One group of experts believes that the well-known Halley's comet was the Star of Bethlehem. In the seventeenth century, Edmund Halley noticed that three comets had appeared in 1531, 1607 and 1682—and he also determined they had been following the same path through space. He correctly concluded that these three comets were actually the same comet appearing on three separate occasions. He then accurately predicted the return of the comet in 1758, and astronomers have observed its arrival every seventy-five to seventy-six years ever since.

Other thinkers then started putting two and two together and decided that perhaps Halley's comet was actually the Star of Bethlehem. They calculated the periodic appearances of this comet back through history and found that ancient chronicles indicate it had probably shown up in 85 B.C. and again in 11 B.C.

Some have argued that 11 B.C. is close enough to the most popular dates for Christ's birth, or 5–4 B.C., for historians to have miscalculated His nativity by six years or so.[4] But our investigation of the acceptable date ranges for Christ's birth has shown it would be highly unlikely, if not impossible, for Christ to have been born before 8 B.C.

But even if Halley's comet wasn't the one, there are other possibilities.

There is one suggestion, for example, that a comet reported by the Jewish historian Josephus, just before the war leading to the destruction of Jerusalem in A.D. 70, may have had some connection to the Star of Bethlehem.[5] One theory is that Josephus had in mind the much earlier light cast by the Bethlehem Star—a light which was actually produced by a comet. Both Josephus and Matthew say that a star "stood over" a certain location, though Matthew has the star over Bethlehem and Josephus has it over Jerusalem.

The problem with this view is that Josephus would have

had to be far out of phase chronologically if he was referring to a comet that appeared in the late first century B.C. And if we try to say that Josephus was actually referring to a comet in A.D. 64, or thereabouts, then Matthew's account of the Star becomes meaningless because the Star would have had to appear long after Christ died.

But there are more reasonable and compelling comet theories than these. One that has captured the imaginations of a few writers is the idea that a comet, or *hui hsing*, sighted by Chinese astronomers in 5 B.C. may have been related to the Star.[6] Chinese records show that this "sweeping star," as the Chinese called it, appeared in the constellation of Capricorn and was visible for more than seventy days. Later, in April of 4 B.C., Chinese astronomers made an entry in their records that a *po hsing*, or a "comet without a tail," appeared in the constellation Aquilla.[7] This second object in the skies, since it lacked the usual tail that comets have, may have been what we would call a nova, or the light from an exploding star in deep space.

Whatever the precise identification, one or both of these Chinese "comets" could have had something to do with what the Magi saw. Here's one scenario that has been proposed:

The Magi, intently scanning the skies over their native Persia, saw the triple conjunction of Jupiter and Saturn in 7 B.C.— the incident we described in some detail in the previous chapter. Their astrological background immediately made them aware that something important was about to happen in Judea, so they set out for Jerusalem.   •

Then they wandered around Jerusalem for a while until Herod finally called them in for an audience. He told them to head for Bethlehem, and as soon as they were out on the road, they looked up into the night sky and saw the "sweeping star," or comet, of 5 B.C. (or perhaps the nova or comet of 4 B.C.). This startling activity in the heavens confirmed to them that they were on the right track. So they forged ahead into Bethlehem, and by making local inquiries they learned that an unusual child, Jesus, had been born recently. People talked about him having a special destiny, and shepherds from the fields—without any urging at all—had come in to worship him.

This may seem to tie everything up into a nice neat package, but there are a number of serious problems with this story line—and any theory, for that matter, that makes comets a key feature in identifying the Star.

First of all, there's the basic problem with what comets *usually* signified to ancient astronomers and astrologers. As we saw earlier in this chapter, in most instances comets heralded something evil, rather than something good. Josephus, for one, thought the appearances of a comet before the destruction of Jerusalem was an evil sign—and it would be hard to argue with that interpretation if you happened to be under siege in Jerusalem in A.D. 70.

This same fear of comets extended well into the medieval period, too. For example, a comet appeared in the skies as William the Conqueror invaded England in 1066, and the fright inspired by this sight caused his enemies on the island to lose heart. They literally threw down their arms and ran away in the face of the opposition they perceived not only from a man but from the heavens as well.

Those who argue that comets can also have a positive interpretation, especially as far as the birth of kings is concerned, cite the tradition that a comet may have announced the birth and accession to the throne of Mithradates the Great, the king of Parthia (Persia). He is supposed to have been born in 134 B.C. and become king in 120 B.C., and Chinese records indicate that comets appeared on both these dates.[8] There is still another tradition that when Augustus Caesar began his imperial reign, another comet streaked into the skies overhead.

But the weight of tradition and authority is solidly in favor of an evil interpretation of comets, and that's one major factor that makes the comet approach rather weak. It could conceivably be argued that since the Magi were Persians and Mithradates the Great was a Persian king, they might have been more attuned to the positive interpretation of comets. And it is true that this Mithradates was quite successful in defeating Persia's enemies and entering into fruitful negotiations with the Romans, who were seen as a threat to Persian safety.

But remember: The Magi were broadly educated intellectuals who probably had the highest ideals in mind for what their Savior or Sosiosh would be like. They must have seen that He would be far superior to any earthly ruler up to that point. And they would more than likely have expected any sign signaling His birth in the heavens to be unequivocally positive—not an exception to a preponderance of evil omens.

The date is right for the Chinese comets—5 B.C. and 4 B.C. (if the later one really *was* a comet—there's a better argument that it was a nova, as we'll see in the next chapter). But there are still other problems that undercut the "sweeping star" theory.

A comet in itself wouldn't have prompted the Magi to head for Judea, so it would have had to be combined with a conjunction, as in one scenario we've already suggested. But even with an appropriate conjunction, a comet simply doesn't fit into the clear historical Biblical account. Remember that neither Herod nor the chief priests nor the scribes were aware of any unusual astronomical happening, and they would certainly have known something about a comet. If you have any doubts, make a date to take a look at Halley's comet when it passes over on its next trip by earth in 1985–86. Despite our relative lack of concern with the movements of the heavens, it's hard not to be impressed by a sight like that.

Also, the notion that the Magi may have made it to Bethlehem but then had to inquire around about Jesus' house runs against the clear words of the second chapter of Matthew. The Gospel says that the Star stood over the place where the child was—and that would be an extremely hard trick for any comet.

One directional feature a comet has going for it is its tail, and since that tail always points away from the sun, the Magi may have been traveling when the tail was "gesturing" toward Bethlehem from Jerusalem. But when they arrived in Bethlehem, they would have confronted the same problem with a comet that they would have faced with a conjunction, a single planet, a star, a meteor or a bolide: How could a comet have pointed out the house? Unless we fall back on some weak, shadow-and-light theory, where Jesus' house was highlighted by a quirk of star and comet light, there's no way there could have been a directional beam.

So we seem to find ourselves back at square one. Any of these theories so far are possible if we just bend the facts a little or let our imaginations run so free that we enter the realm of wild speculation. But this is not the way to resolve as important an issue as the Star of Bethlehem, which purportedly announced the most important event in the history of man. The "scientific" line of investigation can't be considered complete, though, before we look at one more natural interpretation of the Star—an interpretation that seems to satisfy more people than any other.

CHAPTER TEN

EXPLOSIONS IN DEEP SPACE

If you have some old Christmas cards, pull them out and see if there are any pictures of the wise men and the Star of Bethlehem.

If you can find such a card, the chances are that the star is pictured as a huge, radiant, fixed star in the heavens, emitting almost as much light as the full moon. This kind of portrayal may seem too literal and even simplistic, but actually, it may be quite accurate if the Star of Bethlehem was really an *explosion in deep space*, or what astronomers call a nova or a supernova.

In the first chapter, we described what science-fiction writer Arthur C. Clarke imagined as the explosion of a supernova in deep space. The journey of the light from that explosion took more than three thousand years to get to earth, where the wise men perceived it as the Star of Bethlehem. But there are other important dimensions to the nova and supernova theories.

First of all, the fact that Matthew seems to speak of the Star as something new and unexpected seems to fit right into the nova or supernova approach. There are several types of unusual "new" stars that vary in light intensity and may pulsate or erupt when they first appear. Many of the so-called *variable stars*, which change their luminosity on a periodic or erratic basis, aren't bright enough to be regarded as spectacular celestial events. But novas and supernovas have been known to achieve unusual brightness within very short periods of time.

A nova—the word is Latin for "new"—is an existing star that suddenly emits an unusual outburst of light. Sometimes, a star that's too faint even to be visible to the naked eye suddenly attains enough brightness to be visible for days or weeks before fading from sight again. The short duration of these stars caused the Chinese to dub them "guest stars."[1]

During its major outburst of light, a nova typically flares up to thousands or even tens of thousands of times its original brightness. The rise to maximum light is very rapid—sometimes taking less than one day. Scientists differ on the mechanism that starts the chain of explosions that results in a nova, but they agree that when the great burst of light occurs, an outer section or layer of the star blasts off as an expanding, luminous gas.

Novas usually aren't visible to the naked eye, and many completely escape detection by our astronomers. As a matter of fact, only two or three are usually found each year by telescope.

An appearance of a supernova is an even rarer event. While an ordinary nova may increase its brilliance to as much as twenty-five thousand times our own sun's luminosity, a supernova can flare up to hundreds of millions of times its original brightness, or often more than 100 million times our own sun's light. It has been estimated that if a star a hundred light-years away from earth became a supernova, it would be brighter than the full moon in our night skies.

So you can see the point about traditional Christmas cards depicting the Star and the wise men. If the Star of Bethlehem really was a supernova, it could have shone down on the Magi in much the way those quaint little cards suggest.

In technical terms, a supernova is a star, like our sun, that has used up its nuclear fuel, collapsed into a highly concentrated state and finally exploded in one last huge burst of energy. The star's particles and gases would be ejected at incredible rates of speed—up to three thousand miles per second. The final result would be an expanding cloud of luminous gases—called a "nebula"—and also a small, burned-up solid object in the middle of the gas. If this relatively small solid residue of the star continues to give off radio signals—signals that pulse as the object spins around—then the solid residue of the explosion is called a *pulsar*.[2]

Many novas have been observed throughout history, but only a very small number of the "big blast" supernovas have been recorded in our galaxy. The earliest, and perhaps the brightest, recorded supernova occurred in the constellation Vega several thousand years ago. The record of this event is an ancient Sumerian tablet which shows an extremely bright star in the constellation.[3] The explosion in the sky became quite an important factor in Sumerian mythology.

Another striking supernova blasted forth in the eleventh century A.D.—the so-called *Crab nebula* in the constellation Taurus, in 1054.

This 1054 supernova is particularly interesting because an understanding of the impact it had can help us deal more effectively with the nova theory of the Star of Bethlehem. Chinese and Japanese astronomers kept rather detailed records of the event, and some American Indian rock tablets may also refer to this supernova. But inexplicably, European stargazers seem to have completely ignored it.

This is hard to understand because, according to the Chinese, the exploding star was actually visible during the day for about twenty-three days and at night for about six months. Then, as the gases began to spread out in space from the explosion, a nebula formed which is hard to miss.[4] In our own day it has been nicknamed the Crab nebula because it seems to have the shape of a crab.

One sighting of this supernova outside the Far East recently came to light when a discovery was made of records kept by an Iraqi physician named Ibn Butlan, who was living in Constantinople in 1054. Although not an astronomer or astrologer, Butlan was deeply interested in establishing connections between heavenly events and human health.

"One of the well-known epidemics of our own time," he wrote, "is that which occurred when the spectacular star appeared in Gemini in the year 446 H. (or April 14, 1054, to April 1, 1055). In the autumn of that year, 14,000 people were buried in the Church of Luke after all the cemeteries in Constantinople had been filled."[5]

This association of a supernova with earth-shaking events— even if they were quite negative in the form of an epidemic— reflects a likely reaction of any observer, including the Magi of Christ's time. Of even more interest, though, is the fact that such an apparently spectacular event was so sparsely recorded. If references to the 1054 supernova were so scanty, it seems equally possible that there might be little or no documentation of a similar heavenly occurrence back in 4 B.C. or thereabouts.

Descriptions of a couple of later supernovas—the so-called *Tycho's star* of 1572 and the 1604 supernova which, as we mentioned earlier, Johannes Kepler described—can teach us some further things about these explosions in deep space. The 1572 event was observed in the constellation Cassiopeia by the Danish astronomer Tycho Brahe. The new star lasted for several months and was brighter than any of the other planets, including Venus. It was even visible during daylight. A French reformer, Theodore Beza, immediately started making Biblical connections and began to proclaim that this supernova was really the Star of Bethlehem, which had come back to mark the beginning of a new Christian age. Beza thus joined forces with Kepler, who also believed the supernova he observed with the planetary conjunction in the constellation

Ophiuchus in 1604 might have something to do with the Star of Bethlehem.

But was the Star of Bethlehem a supernova?

The only recorded candidates for novas—and not necessarily supernovas—at the times we've set for the birth of Christ are those recorded in Chinese records in March of 5 B.C. and April 4 B.C. Either of these objects could have been a comet or a nova, though probably the former was a comet and the latter was a nova. But even if we don't have a record of another nova or supernova during the period 8–4 B.C., that doesn't mean there wasn't one. Remember the lack of records for the spectacular 1054 event!

One of the strongest cases we've come across that the Star may have been a nova or supernova goes something like this:

The Magi saw a nova or supernova, possibly in a constellation or planetary grouping they interpreted as connected in some way with Judea. The nova appeared first in the east as a "morning star," but was only visible for a few days before it faded to its original dimness. During this brief flare-up, only the Magi saw the Star because there was a heavy cloud covering over most of Palestine. As a result, when the Magi reached Jerusalem and started asking questions about the "star in the east," nobody knew what they were talking about.

The Magi then had their meeting with Herod and his advisers and headed out toward Bethlehem. The same supernova flared up again, but this time in the clear skies over Judea and in a direct line with Bethlehem. Some novas have indeed been known to flare up, die down and then flare up again on a separate occasion.

Then, when the Magi reached Bethlehem, they discovered through a brief investigation which house seemed most likely to house the infant Messiah, and sure enough, as they stood in front of Jesus' home, the same nova they had been "following" seemed to be resting out in the distance just over the roof of His house.

The miracle in this scenario would be in the timing of the

nova flare-ups and the convenient cloud covering over Palestine. Obviously if the second flare-up took place *after* the Magi left Herod, there would be no problem with Herod and his advisers seeing it. The Bible says only that he was unaware of the Star *at the time of his meeting* with the wise men, not that he didn't see a star after they left him.

But there are still several difficulties with this approach. For one thing, the explanation that the Star merely confirmed the wise men's prior discovery of Jesus' whereabouts seems a little weak. To compensate for this problem, some proponents of the nova theory have suggested that the nova may have been seen among a group of stars within the constellation Cancer which ancient astronomers designated as the "manger." If this had been the case, the nova in a "heavenly manger" would have suggested to the Magi that they look for the Messiah in a *real* manger in Bethlehem.[6] Unfortunately, those who support this interpretation are operating in the wrong Gospel. It's the Book of Luke that refers to a manger. Matthew says Jesus and his mother Mary were in a *house*—apparently they had moved into better quarters since His birth as it was described in Luke. So if the Magi had started searching around in Bethlehem's various mangers, they would have come up empty-handed.

Although a number of proponents of the exploding star theory believe a nova (rather than a supernova) might have been the Star, it probably just wouldn't have had enough impact to make sophisticated astronomers and astrologers like the Magi believe a Savior had been born. Novas are generally rather dull events. They would never inspire a popular artist to put together a dramatic Christmas card!

Also, there were simply too many novas bursting forth in the skies to make anybody sit up and take notice. Probable novas were recorded in 69, 48 and 4 B.C., and also in A.D. 29 and 70, to name just a few in that general period. Surely, if the greatest birth in the history of the world was about to be announced, something more appropriate than a mere nova would be used—or so many ancient stargazers might have reasoned.

So we're left with a supernova if we want this theory of the Star to make sense. But one major problem here is that apparently none was recorded at the right time. The Chinese *po hsing* of 4 B.C., or the "comet without a tail," might have been a nova, though from the recorded description it's unlikely it was as spectacular as a supernova would have been. Also, even if it was a supernova, there's a problem with the date of this "new star." Herod died in late March or early April of 4 B.C., and yet the nova also appeared in April of 4 B.C. That would leave very little time for a necessary series of incidents, recorded in Matthew and Luke, which must have occurred after the appearance of the Star but before Herod's death. These include the arrival and departure of the Magi; the various warnings to Joseph and the Magi in dreams; the flight of the Holy Family to Egypt; and the killing of the male children in Bethlehem. This just seems too much to have happening in that particular time frame.

The supernova theory of the Star of Bethlehem is certainly one of the most attractive presented thus far—especially if it's combined with one of the conjunction approaches that we discussed in earlier chapters. And tradition—especially the image of the Star and the wise men we all remember from our Christmas cards as children—has a strong pull.

But there are too many holes in this interpretation for us to be satisfied that we've finally found the ultimate answer in our search for the true identity of the Star.

Those three key tests that we set up at the beginning of our search—tests that are firmly grounded in Matthew's account—still haven't been adequately passed. First of all, the fact that the Star Matthew describes failed to catch the attention of the general public casts a shadow of doubt on all the strongest astronomical theories. If the star or conjunction or fireball or nova was up there in the sky, why was there complete ignorance of it in the court of Herod?

Secondly, the Star disappeared and then reappeared—a peculiar quality for an ordinary celestial body. There are some possible natural explanations for this kind of activity, such as novas that flare up, die down and flare up again, or perhaps a series of planetary conjunctions or meteor showers. But all these explanations seem a little strained.

Finally, the toughest test—and the one where all the natural explanations seem to fall short—is the requirement that the Star have a directional or guided light that "put the finger," so to speak, on the Messiah's house. You may try to argue—as we've seen different experts do—that light and shadows fell on Jesus' house in a certain way, or that the Magi actually carried out an investigation of His whereabouts, or that they took an astronomical sighting from a deep well. Somehow, though, those explanations just don't satisfy.

But even if the natural, scientific interpretations fall short, isn't there another possible channel of inquiry? What about what might be called the "extranatural" or paranormal explanations of strange happenings that we hear so often these days?

Our search for the Star of Bethlehem now seems to be leading us into those uncharted waters, where the hard reality of the scientific present merges into strange speculations about what might be the reality of the future.

CHAPTER ELEVEN

A VISITOR FROM OUTER SPACE?

The three Persian priests pored over their charts and diagrams of the heavens. Some interesting things had been happening in their night skies during the past few months—especially that triple conjunction of Jupiter and Saturn—and they had developed a sense of expectation.

Of course, the expectation that they were on the verge of something cataclysmic in world history had been with them a long time. But something more immediate seemed to be in the air, in the minds of common people as well as intellectuals like themselves. Unless you could pin these vague feelings down by a definite, clear event in the heavens or some other sign, though, the feelings weren't worth much.

They believed the Sosiosh, or world Savior, would eventually come. Their Zoroastrian beliefs had convinced them of that. But was the Savior's appearance imminent? There was uncertainty. Still, it was a time to watch the heavens, wait patiently and be sure they didn't miss anything important. After all, the responsibility for interpreting global movements had been entrusted to them and others of the Magus caste. If they failed in this duty, they failed in their fundamental purpose for even existing.

So they decided once again—as they had done for so many nights during the past years—to man their observation post under the stars. One man would be enough. The chances were that the heavens would move inexorably and deliberately but slowly that evening, as they did most evenings. Barring the appearance of a meteor shower or a fireball, whatever appeared tonight would more than likely be there tomorrow night.

It was the youngest priest's turn, and frankly, he wasn't really looking forward to his assignment. He enjoyed studying the heavens, but libraries and scrolls and intellectual gymnastics with the two older Magi were his preferences. Basically, he just wasn't an outdoorsman, and even though he knew on-the-spot observation was essential for him to excel at his calling, he would always choose his warm study over the cool, clammy, bug-infested Persian nights.

The stars were marvelous that night, however. Falling stars, or meteors, streaked across the sky several times each hour, and the shining gods in the heavens seemed to be so clear and close that he almost felt he could touch them.

But what was that? He sat up straight and watched awestruck as a strange luminous new star appeared before him. It moved with blinding speed from one constellation to the next. A falling star in the background seemed to be traveling in slow motion in comparison. Then the object got much larger and changed from its original circular shape to a more oblong form.

The priest staggered to his feet and watched with his mouth agape as the object, now even larger than the moon, stopped motionless over his head. He uttered a brief prayer to this miraculous new god and waited silently to see if there would be any communication. And there was, but not quite through the sort of channels he would have expected.

There was no booming voice or piercing sound of trumpets, as he would have thought appropriate to herald a miraculous appearance. Instead, he felt his mind being grasped—that was the only way he knew to describe the experience afterward. And he knew—he absolutely *knew*—that his instructions were to rouse his fellow priests and prepare immediately for a trip to Jerusalem to greet the newborn Savior, who was also "king of the Jews."

The other Magi were somewhat skeptical and disgruntled when the younger man waked them up in such a state of fearful excitement. They secretly suspected he had just fallen asleep at his post and then had a vivid dream that seemed real enough to be true.

But when they followed their brother priest outside, their skepticism vanished. The luminous, oval-shaped "star" was still there. And as if to confirm the message about traveling immediately to Jerusalem, the new star darted with incredible speed toward the west, in precisely the direction of Judea, and then flashed back again overhead.

The Magi quickly packed up and headed toward Judea— but they didn't see the "star" again until they arrived at their destination. When called before Herod, they could only tell him that they had received a divine message about the birth of "the king of the Jews"—no offense intended toward Herod, of course, since they knew he also had been awarded that title by the Romans. And they told him about the Messiah's strange "star" that they had seen. But, Herod didn't know what they were talking about since the "star" had appeared only in Persia.

After receiving directions from Herod that Hebrew prophecies indicated the Messiah was supposed to be born in Bethlehem, the Magi immediately set out on the short six-mile trek to that town. And to their surprise and joy, the same luminous body that they had seen in Persia appeared once again and directed them silently into the center of Bethlehem. Finally, the luminous object—which seemed to change colors and also occasionally even changed shape—from the oblong, to the oval or even circular, and back to the oblong—stopped. And then the most amazing thing happened. A bright beam burst forth from the "star" and illuminated one small home in the town of Bethlehem. There was no doubt what their objective was now. The Magi rushed over to that unassuming house, entered and found a young woman cuddling an infant boy, who looked less than a year old. Here, finally, was the Messiah they had been looking for. And they soon learned his name was Jesus and his mother was called Mary.

This scenario may seem to be the most farfetched notion we've attempted yet in this book. But the general picture that's been sketched coincides with what many sane people say they have experienced and seen in contacts with unidentified flying objects, or "UFO's."

There have been reports of UFO's at different points throughout history, but the recent wave of interest in the subject was sparked in June of 1947 when a young amateur pilot named Ken Arnold was flying his own plane in the vicinity of Mount Rainier in the State of Washington.[1] In scanning the sky in front of him, he suddenly saw nine shiny, circular objects streak in formation at speeds he guessed were in excess of a thousand miles per hour. The objects moved in a jumpy way, and he described them as "saucers skipping across the water"—hence the derivation of our popular name, "flying saucers."

A majority of the sightings—by an estimated 15 million Americans since Arnold's historic kickoff encounter with those UFO's—have been explained away by scientists and Air Force officials. Some were identified as reflections in the night sky, or ordinary stars, or meteors or whatever. But as many as 20 percent of these sighted objects remain "unidentified," and that leaves a great deal of room for further investigation and speculation about what they actually were.

There are many recorded descriptions of these UFO's. In addition to "flying saucers," they've been referred to as shining spherical objects; circular, somewhat convex disks; cylinders or cigar-shaped objects; and oval-shaped "flying eggs."

Bright lights and colors often accompany their appearances in the sky—halos, luminous tails almost like those of comets, flashing lights and beaming searchlights.

UFO experts have classified three major "encounters" with these objects—you may have heard the descriptions in publicity for the popular science fiction movie *Close Encounters of the Third Kind.* "Close encounters of the first kind" include those in which the UFO is seen at relatively close quarters—as the Magi did initially in our imaginary scenario at the start of the chapter. "Close encounters of the second kind" include those in which the UFO is not only seen but has a certain impact on the environment, such as tearing off limbs of trees, charring the ground or frightening wildlife or domestic animals. "Close encounters of the third kind" involve sighting or having contact with alien creatures who may be operating the strange "spacecraft."

All of these types of "encounters" have been recorded in the UFO investigations, and, whether you believe in them or not, many have not been adequately explained away. Some who claim to have seen and even been temporarily captured by alien creatures have come up with corroborating evidence of one sort or another, including other witnesses, the ability to recount their stories while under medically induced hypnotic trances and unusual physical evidence such as burned areas of forests where the UFO is supposed to have landed.

Needless to say, there is some skepticism about these stories, and there has also been some concern on the part of governmental authorities that too many UFO reports might cause undue fear or even hysteria in the population at large. A concerted U. S. Government effort, designated by the rather unusual name "Project Grudge," was started to discredit the many unexplained UFO reports.[2]

But this effort to put a lid on the intense interest in "ufology" hasn't been at all successful. In fact, it's sometimes gotten rather ludicrous—such as on the occasion in 1956 when a UFO actually was reported to have landed during the day close to the nuclear weapons test site at White Sands, New Mexico. A large number of people, including two Air Force colonels, said they saw the landing, and it has been well documented in government records.[3]

It seems quite possible, then, that UFO's do exist, but what exactly are they?

One popular view is that they are extraterrestrial vehicles manned by creatures of high technological skills and intelligence from faraway galaxies. This extraterrestrial intelligence, or "ETI," explanation has gained a lot of support because there's considerable glamour and excitement about it. Fascination with the exploits of Buck Rogers, Flash Gordon and the crew of *Star Trek* may be a basic reflection of our human need for new frontiers to explore, new worlds to conquer. We don't like the thought that voyages of earlier adventurers such as Columbus and Magellan and Sir Francis Drake may have been the last wave of contact with foreign, exotic, alien peoples. We like to believe the old science fiction cliché "We are not alone." So our reason capitulates to our imagination, and mere speculation becomes firm belief that there are, indeed, intelligent civilizations out there in space—civilizations that are making contact with us through the wave of UFO's.

Despite the wish-fulfillment attraction of this extraterrestrial approach, there are many problems with it.[4] First of all, there is absolutely no evidence that intelligent creatures exist on distant planets. In fact, as of this writing, there is no evidence of life of any sort on other planets. Certainly, there is a great deal of speculation and even expressions of hope by scientists that some sort of life will be found by this or that space probe. But nothing even close to a living organism has been discovered. This is not to say, of course, that extensive efforts aren't being made to establish some sort of communication with civilized creatures who may or may not be out there in deep space. Listening posts have been set up with sophisticated devices that can receive signals from faraway star systems. And plans are in the works to spend ever increasing amounts of government money for these possibly fruitless projects. But so far, no messages have been received. At this stage, the whole effort must be marked down as nothing more than an elaborate attempt at wish fulfillment.

A second point made by opponents of the extraterrestrial intelligence theory is that the mathematical odds are astronomically (an apt adverb) unfavorable for our UFO's being vehicles manned by aliens from outer space. By one estimate, if there are 1 million separate alien civilizations on other planets in our galaxy which are capable of launching spaceships to search for intelligent life elsewhere in the universe, each of these civilizations would have to send out about ten thousand spaceships every year for *one* UFO to make it to our earth every year.[5] Most of the spaceships that didn't make it to earth would supposedly be probing the billions of other planets and solar systems in the universe.

When you consider the small number of space probes we send out, these figures seem absurd on their very face. And there's a highly questionable assumption at the very foundation of such a theory: the idea that there are a million (or even a thousand or a hundred) civilizations in our galaxy which are capable of launching deep-space probes rests on the belief that this many civilizations would have solved their internal problems. In other words, they wouldn't use their technology to destroy themselves, but rather would use it to explore other galaxies. In light of the highly uncertain outcome of our own resolution of the nuclear weapons issue, this assumption seems somewhat questionable.

The usual way that proponents of the extraterrestrial theory respond to these objections is, "You're thinking in terms of our own stage of development rather than the much more highly advanced technologies the UFO's are likely to have. Why, just look at the way they operate—accelerating up to incredible speeds in a matter of seconds, turning on a dime, appearing and disappearing at will. With that kind of science, you're no longer even operating in an earthly dimension. Any civilization with vehicles that can perform like that must surely have solved all problems of time and space exploration that we mere earthlings can imagine."

This brings us to the crux of the matter. It's true that ordinary technology and physical equipment simply can't operate and maneuver the way these UFO's seem to. So, in a sense, that puts them outside the realm of the mere extraterrestrial into what might best be called the *extradimensional*. In other words, we're not dealing simply with machines and creatures basically like those on earth but from a distant solar system. Instead, we're getting involved with something on a completely different plane of life—if "life" in the sense we understand it on earth is really the proper word.

To summarize, here's where all this seems to be leading us: These "visitors from outer space" have arrived here after traversing incredible distance in space, against all mathematical odds. They move about in ways that completely defy all our known laws of physical science. Apparently, they've solved all their problems at home because they've managed to overcome internal strife sufficiently to survive and direct their energies and intelligence toward producing a technology that can seemingly accomplish the impossible.

The reason the term "extradimensional" seems more descriptive of such a civilization than "extraterrestrial" is that, in a sense, we're moving into what might be called a spiritual rather than a scientific area of inquiry. These beings are so advanced and superior to us that we can't describe them in conventional scientific language. That fact in effect forces us to start talking in more philosophical or spiritual terms.

But before we proceed any further with this line of inquiry, here's one word of caution: Don't assume we're moving from the real to the unreal as we shift from the "scientific" to the "spiritual." The reports of those UFO's are as real as the chair you're sitting in. It's just that they can't be explained in quite the same way you'd describe the chair. A different approach must be used, but that doesn't mean we're about to introduce an antiscientific theory. We must go *beyond* the limitations of the scientific method to find the answers we're seeking.

That's part of the reason why we have chosen the word "extradimensional." This term implies something outside our own frame of knowledge and reference, but doesn't by any means connote events or things that are mere fantasy. What the Magi saw nearly two thousand years ago certainly wasn't fantasy. In Matthew's straightforward, factual account, they saw what he called a "star." That word—a catchall term for various luminous heavenly bodies—was broad enough to cover not only the stars and planets and meteors and supernovas, but also what we today call UFO's.

And unlike the normal bodies in our heavens, a UFO could easily have met all the tests Matthew lays down for the Star. It could have appeared and disappeared; it could have made itself visible *only* to the wise men and it could have directed a beam of light down on Jesus' house.

But was the Star really a UFO? If it was, it must not have been "extraterrestrial," because, as we've seen, that term doesn't go quite far enough in explaining the unusual qualities of a UFO. The better term is that it was extradimensional—so unlike us and so advanced technologically over anything we can even imagine that our normal scientific terms don't apply.

Now let's cast all our assumptions about conventional science aside and follow our search for the Star into this other dimension of reality—where even angels may fear to tread.

CHAPTER TWELVE

WHERE ANGELS
FEAR TO TREAD

At the beginning of the previous chapter, the young Persian priest studying the heavens suddenly saw a strange, luminous body that could move back and forth at incredible speed. It could appear and disappear and even communicate through some sort of telepathic communication. This "star," as the priest and his brother Magi came to call it, also directed a beam of light down to the ground in Bethlehem and thereby identified the house where Jesus was staying with His parents.

One interpretation of this "star" is that it might have been an extraterrestrial vehicle from some faraway planet, many light-years out in deep space. But, as we've seen, there are an overwhelming number of problems with this theory.

On the other hand, if the "star" had been an extradimensional, rather than an extraterrestrial UFO, we wouldn't be bothered with the problem of a "spaceship" of some sort getting here to earth from deep space. Rather, the UFO could slip into our sight, into our reality, almost instantaneously from *another* reality—perhaps from some sort of "parallel universe."

The idea of a separate dimension of reality—a parallel universe existing side by side with or even in the same space as ours—has intrigued scientists and science fiction writers for years. It would work something like this: Beings and objects with a different or separate dimension from our three dimensions of height, depth and width might occupy the same space we do, except in a different way. The extra dimension might have something to do with time, since we're limited and controlled by time and an eternal or timeless creature wouldn't be. Or there might be another or many other separate dimensions of reality that we can't even imagine.

To illustrate this point, imagine a world in the midst of ours that has only two-dimensional objects and people.[1] In other words, everything is flatter than a sheet of paper, with width and depth but no height. Of course, the beings in that "Flatland" world can perceive each other only in two-dimensional terms, too. They don't understand the third dimension of height because they don't have it and are unable to see it even if it appears right in front of them.

But then you, as a three-dimensional human being, move into their space. You can see much more of them than they can see of themselves because you can look down on them and under them, while they can only see one another's borders in their paper-thin, two-dimensional reality. And since you're now standing in their space they can see you too—but only a very small and distorted cross section of your body. To understand this, imagine that you're wading up to your waist in a perfectly smooth pool of water. The surface of the water is touching your forearms and waist, but that's all; and someone wearing special goggles at the water level can only see the parts of your body touching the water at water level.

The perspective of the person with the goggles would be something like that of the two-dimensional creature watching you enter his space. He would actually see three objects: two of them would be the same size, but they would be smaller than the third object. These, of course, would be the outlines of your forearms and your waist. But the two-dimensional being wouldn't have the slightest idea of what the rest of you

—your feet and shoulders and head—looked like. In fact, if someone tried to explain, the message simply couldn't get through because he would have no means of perceiving or comprehending what the third dimension involved.

In this example, you and the two-dimensional "person" would coexist in the same space, at the same time, but your extra dimension of reality would put you completely outside his frame of reference, except insofar as you chose to intrude into his two-dimensional world.

The many UFO's that have been sighted throughout history may have the same relationship to us as we would have to the two-dimensional beings in the illustration. Somehow, they enter our three-dimensional world through a "door" of some sort from their four- (or more) dimensional world. We see them partially, in bits and pieces as our perceptions allow, but much of their reality remains beyond us. Yet they occupy the same space we do, only outside our perceptions in their additional dimensions of existence.

An attempt to explain the Star of Bethlehem in extradimensional terms has been made by Barry H. Downing in his book *The Bible and Flying Saucers*.[2] Downing first relates some Old Testament occurrences, such as the "pillar of fire" and "pillar of cloud" that led the Israelites in the wilderness, to the UFO's that we see today. He then draws a parallel between such Old Testament events in the skies and the angel appearing in the "glory of the Lord" in the second chapter of Luke. Downing suggests that there may be a connection between these two bright heavenly occurrences, and that both may be the same type of UFO.

Then he briefly mentions the Star of Bethlehem and stresses, as we have done, that no ordinary star could have come to rest over the house of Jesus. He concludes, ". . . if beings from another world deliberately sought to draw attention to the birth of Christ, a space vehicle answering the description of modern UFOs would have been capable of carrying out the activities which the Bible describes: transporting

beings from another world to instruct shepherds, lead Wise
Men with some type of starlike beacon, or even bring Gabriel
to meet Mary."

Downing's theory seems a strange mixture of the extraterrestrial and extradimensional approaches. He talks about
UFO's and their occupants as though they were essentially
like the space vehicles and beings of earth, except more
highly developed. But at the same time, he clearly believes
that the realm from which they come—heaven, that is—is a parallel dimension to our own earthly existence. These UFO's and
their pilots and passengers look and behave much as we and
our machines do—yet somehow, in a way Downing never
completely explains, they have dimensions to their reality that
we don't have.

But the most serious problem with Downing's thesis, and
with any theory that sees the UFO phenomenon as basically a
good thing, is that the recent evidence gathered about UFO's
suggests the contrary.

To demonstrate this point, let's take a closer look at some
descriptions of various encounters with UFO's. One recurring
observation is that often a UFO may seem abnormal, in the
sense that it almost seems alive or organic. Some observers
have noticed that they change shape or undulate. And certainly, the abrupt movements of these objects almost suggest
some sort of interstellar insect as they accelerate from standing still to moving fifteen thousand miles per hour or more in
just seconds, and then turn at right angles or abruptly reverse
direction.

These descriptions, in themselves, aren't particularly negative. But they do stand in stark contrast to the idea that
UFO's are just a higher form of "vehicle," much like our own
except far more advanced. Rather than some kind of spaceship carrying alien beings, the UFO's seem more like the
beings themselves. And their ability to change lights and
shapes and speeds so abruptly might even suggest the in-

trusion into our space of extradimensional creatures rather than a group of transport ships.

If this is the true nature of UFO's, then most of us have been deceived about their identity all these years. Either we've simply deceived ourselves, or just as likely, the UFO's have been deceiving us or consciously allowing us to continue in our self-deceptions.

Some of the accounts of actual encounters with these UFO's are a much more ominous problem. UFO landing areas, where they have reportedly actually touched ground, are characterized by destruction and mutilation. Horrible odors often pervade the air; dead, mutilated animals may lie strewn about; the ground and foliage may be destroyed through burning.[3]

The effect on human beings isn't particularly pleasant, either. Some nearby observers have suffered paralysis, eye inflammations, first-degree burns on the skin and a variety of emotional upsets (from simple fear to hysteria and headaches that may plague the victims for months afterward).

There are also a number of accounts of "abductions" of humans by the UFO's. Whether or not these are actually true or merely some sort of emotional aberration in the individuals involved, they still follow the same basically negative pattern. In one case, a man named Brian Scott claimed to have been abducted by a UFO on five occasions in Arizona and California, during the period 1971 to 1975.[4] The first time, he said, he was lifted in the air into a two-hundred-foot-wide flying saucer. He found himself lying down, completely paralyzed, in a small room. Several very tall, ugly beings, with sloping shoulders and crocodile-scaled skin entered and proceeded to undress him. Heavy fog or mist swirled around him.

Scott said he felt a series of uncomfortable sensations from his feet upward and thought he was probably bleeding. He also urinated involuntarily and seemed to feel water running from his stomach. He also felt his chest being opened and thought his heart had been briefly lifted from his body. Then, his head was pulled about violently, and he smelled a very unpleasant odor.

Finally, an even larger "crocodile" being than the first ones entered and began to communicate telepathically, mind to mind. The message involved some general things about where the aliens came from and what their purpose was and then concluded with a promise that they would return.

Scott was taken away by these aliens on four later occasions and soon found many aspects of his life were controlled by them. He fell into periodic trances in which he produced automatic writing and highly detailed drawings of scientific devices. The aliens have also offered him revelations involving the design of advanced machines, genetic engineering procedures and other such information. These experiences, though, reportedly robbed Scott of his peace of mind. On the whole, they were much more negative than positive encounters.

The strange interactions of Brian Scott with these alien presences are by no means unique, either. Numerous other "close encounters of the third kind" have been reported, sometimes with similar features to the Scott case and sometimes with even more weird and sweeping claims and promises by the aliens.[5] In a number of cases, the aliens make general statements that they want to help mankind and share their vastly superior knowledge. They also frequently promise that those whom they contact will be awarded a special, superior role as mediators between them and other human beings. Sometimes, the aliens even claim to speak for God.

If it weren't for the unpleasant side effects of associating with these UFO's, there might be an unqualified enthusiasm about having been chosen to be among their key contacts on earth. In fact, even with the disconcerting and uncomfortable elements, it might still all be worthwhile if there were a possibility you were really getting in touch with a beneficent higher power.

But even though this "power" behind UFO's may be superior in many ways, a close examination shows it is anything

but beneficent. Think about it for a moment. Those who have
seen or contacted UFO's and their alien "crews" talk about
glowing, shape-changing objects and creatures in the skies.
UFO involvement may be surrounded by foul odors, mutilation of animals, levitation (as Brian Scott was lifted in the air
into a "spaceship"), automatic writing, abuse of the human
body, alteration of the natural laws of science and physics and
inhuman creatures and apparitions.

Sound familiar? It should, because these and other descriptions of encounters with UFO's and their aliens are quite similar to abnormal phenomena and practices that are often connected with the occult and Satan worship.

We've come quite a long way from a cool, scientific ap-
praisal of comets and conjunctions, haven't we? Yet we would
be remiss in any thorough search for the Star of Bethlehem if
we failed to consider the full implications of tying the Star in
with unidentified flying objects. For if we make that mistake,
we may well be falling into the trap that the Bible outlines so
clearly, in so many different passages.

It all got started when the serpent told Eve, in tempting her
with the fruit, "For God knows that when you eat of it your
eyes will be opened, and you will be like God, knowing good
and evil." (Genesis 3:5 NIV) That was the first great deception by Satan—that he could give us special knowledge that
would make us similar to God. That claim has a disturbing
echo in the reported promises made by the aliens from certain
UFO's.[6]

But the warning signals aren't limited to the Old Testament.
These words by the Apostle Paul also have an ominously familiar ring: ". . . for even Satan disguises himself as an angel
of light. Therefore it is not surprising if his servants also dis-
guise themselves as servants of righteousness." (2 Corinthians
11:14–15 NASB)

It all goes back to the basic nature of the Evil One. He's
tricky and deceptive. Or, as John puts it in Revelation 12:9:
"And the great dragon was thrown down, the serpent of old

who is called the devil and Satan, who deceives the whole
world; he was thrown down to the earth, and his angels were
thrown down with him." (NASB)

So the ultimate instigators of evil, not of good, appear to be
behind the UFO phenomenon. And this is the overall situation
they are presenting to us: "The coming of the lawless one will
be in accordance with the work of Satan displayed in all kinds
of counterfeit miracles, signs and wonders, and in every sort
of evil that deceives those who are perishing. They perish because they refused to love the truth and so be saved." (2
Thessalonians 2:9–10 NIV) "Put on the full armor of God so
that you can take your stand against the devil's schemes. For
our struggle is not against flesh and blood, but against the
rulers, against the authorities, against the powers of this dark
world and against the spiritual forces of evil in the heavenly
realms. Therefore put on the full armor of God, so that when
the day of evil comes, you may be able to stand your ground,
and after you have done everything, to stand." (Ephesians
6:11–13 NIV)

It's a frightening outlook, isn't it? The evidence is mounting
that those benign UFO's are probably anything but what they
seem. And if the UFO's are indeed from Satan, it would be
the mistake of the millennium to confound them with that ultimate symbol of good, the Star of Bethlehem.

In fact, everything we know about the nature of the Star
separates it from the "flying saucer" phenomenon. The Magi
were looking for a Sosiosh, or Savior, to deliver them and indeed, all the world, from the inadequate earthly rulers they
had had up to that point. They wanted to find and worship a
supremely good leader, not some evil political or military
genius.

And the Magi were good men themselves. They went to
Herod hoping for the best from him, but when they discovered how evil he was, they disobeyed his instructions to report
back to him and escaped from Judea—probably thus putting
their own lives in jeopardy.

Herod, in his wrath upon learning the Magi had tricked him, ordered that all the male children under two in Bethlehem be killed. That was clearly the most evil act in this entire narrative and it neatly caps the comparison between good and evil, between the Star and Herod in the story. The mysterious, luminous body in Matthew's account was a pointer to good: it alerted the Magi to the birth of a Messiah, filled them with joy on its reappearance and finally guided them to Jesus.

So, intriguing as the UFO theory of the Star may be in some respects, it must be rejected because it falls short in the face of the most crucial test of all: the identification with good or with evil. All indications point toward UFO's being extradimensional, evil objects or forces. In Biblical terms, there is every reason to think they may actually be demonic. They may be part of the dark arsenal that Satan is marshaling to deceive mankind in his effort to gain victory in the massive spiritual warfare that is even now being waged and which may well culminate in a decisive and cataclysmic battle in the near future. But more about this later.

For the moment, it's essential that we know as much as possible about the likely source of UFO's. But the purpose of that knowledge must be to understand how to combat them, not consort with them. Otherwise, we may find ourselves ignoring, to our own danger and detriment, that warning issued by Alexander Pope back in the seventeenth century: "For *fools rush in* where angels fear to tread."

PART THREE

THE ONCE AND FUTURE STAR

CHAPTER THIRTEEN

IT DIDN'T BEGIN IN BETHLEHEM

The Magi were so impressed by the Savior's "star in the east" that they traveled all the way from Persia to Judea just so they could worship Him. Then the Star disappeared before they reached Jerusalem but reappeared as they were heading toward Bethlehem. This second appearance touched them so deeply that they were "overjoyed," according to Matthew.

But what was the Star?

We know it's unlikely the Star was a meteor, or a bolide, or a single planet, or a conjunction of planets, or a supernova, or any other "natural" or known heavenly body. We also know it wasn't an unidentified flying object—at least not in the sense that term is used in describing "flying saucers" and other such weird aerial phenomena.

But now that we've eliminated all these candidates for that famous light in the sky, what are we left with?

First of all, the Star of Bethlehem had a number of distinctive qualities that put it outside the realm of normal astronomical science: it was highly mobile; it had the ability to convey a message about the Messiah and direct the Magi to Jerusalem; and it apparently had some sort of directional nature that allowed it to point out Jesus' house.

The Star was also probably "extradimensional" (super-natural) because, even though we have aircraft today that can perform some, if not all, of these functions that the Messiah's light did for the Magi, no such technology existed in Jesus' time. The chances are far too remote, as we've already seen, that extraterrestrial craft could have traveled to earth from a faraway planet to perform the Star's particular task at that particular time. So the Star must have slipped almost instan-taneously into our earth's time frame from an entirely different dimension—such as a parallel universe.

But unlike the UFO's we examined in previous chapters, this extradimensional light that guided the wise men was a good, positive thing.

So what remains is this: The Star witnessed by the Magi was an extradimensional entity guided by apparent purpose that was unequivocally good and beneficial to mankind.

Some may object at this point, "But that's just a fancy way of saying that the Star was a supernatural event—a message or an actual appearance by God to man which has nothing to do with any natural, scientific explanations. You're talking about miracles!"

That's essentially correct, but it's important to understand exactly what supernatural events and miracles are involved in this particular situation. For if the Star of Bethlehem is a su-pernatural happening, so are the many UFO's that are fre-quently being sighted in our own time. The difference is that UFO's apparently originate in a negative supernatural space or dimension, while the Star came from a positive realm.

Words like "supernatural" and "miracle" have acquired a bad name in modern times because they've sometimes er-roneously been associated with events and beliefs that seem antiscientific or even unreal. But when you think about phe-nomena such as UFO's or the Star in more specific terms—such as the likelihood that they may enter our existence from an ex-tradimensional, parallel universe—the "supernatural" some-

times becomes much more plausible, even if not understandable.

The Star of Bethlehem and UFO's aren't antiscientific; it's
just that they can't be explained or understood in any terms
that our present scientific knowledge or terminology can
grasp. In a sense, they're actually *beyond* science. And they're
certainly not unreal, at least not to those who are willing to
keep an open mind about the reality of both the historical evidence for the Star and more recent evidence for UFO's.

But even in the face of the solidly historical account in
Matthew, and the difficulties inherent in the "scientific" explanations of the Star, some Star theorists are still violently opposed to any extradimensional—or what you might call also
supernatural or miraculous—interpretation.

One type of argument against the supernatural approach
focuses on the text of the Gospel account. Here's the way it
usually goes: First of all, there is no explicit statement in
Matthew that the appearance of the Star involved a miracle.
The point is that Matthew would have given a clear indication if this momentous event in the heavens had been anything other than an ordinary heavenly body of some sort.

Secondly, God chose to reveal His message to a particular
class of people—Magi who had a special knowledge of the
heavens and astrology. If their skills weren't necessary, why
not just pick some ordinary person on the street—perhaps another group from the working class, such as the shepherds?
Because Magi were chosen, the argument goes, it's likely their
educational background and experience with the heavens
gave them some advantage in understanding the message and
meaning of the Star.

In the third place, it's out of line to regard the Star as a supernatural event, because the literal description of the Star in
Matthew seems to be more that of a natural phenomenon
than a miracle.

Fourthly, if the Star *was* a miracle, the message it conveyed
to the Magi would also have had to be communicated in some

extraordinary or miraculous way—but there's no indication of any such unusual communication.

Finally, perhaps the Bible records only what the Magi thought they saw or perceived. In other words, the Star just *seemed* to be moving "ahead of them" and merely appeared to stop over the spot where the child was.

Although each of these objections may seem to have some merit on first glance, a closer look reveals some serious flaws. Let's take each of the five points in order and see how they stand up under scrutiny.

• There's no need for Matthew to say explicitly "this is a miracle" as a prerequisite for the Star to have been one. As a matter of fact, there are many other places in the Bible which speak of supernatural events without calling them "miracles" or "signs." For example, Jesus chose to pay a half-shekel tax in Capernaum, but he picked a rather unusual—in fact, a clearly supernatural—way to get the money. He told Peter, "Go to the sea, and throw in a hook, and take the first fish that comes up, and when you open its mouth, you will find a stater; take that and give it to them for you and me." (Matthew 17:27 NASB)

But even though Jesus was obviously relying on some sort of extranatural or supernatural knowledge about the fact that that particular fish had swallowed money, nothing in the text says it was supernatural or miraculous. The same point might be made of Jesus' feeding of the five thousand and of the four thousand. Each time, with a few loaves and fish, a multitude of people had enough to eat, yet Mark in his Gospel account never mentioned anything about the miraculous nature of those events. (Mark 6:34–44; 8:1–9)

The reason the account of the Star should be taken as miraculous is not because Matthew expressly says it is but because there are no natural phenomena which can adequately explain the facts as presented.

• As for the argument that God wouldn't have chosen astrologers or astronomers unless He meant to use their skills, remember this: The Magi were probably Zoroastrian priests who had been trained and conditioned to look for a Savior whose appearance might be announced in a miraculous way—perhaps even by some sort of shining wheel in the sky.

But in a way, it really doesn't matter what the educational background of the Magi was. God has always had a way of choosing people regardless of their backgrounds, and sometimes even when they seem quite ill fitted for the jobs He calls them to. One of the most dramatic examples that comes to mind is the great Hebrew judge and general Gideon, who was a lowly wine-press worker when the Lord approached him. Gideon, aware of his shortcomings, replied, "Pray, Lord, how can I deliver Israel? Behold, my clan is the weakest in Manasseh, and I am the least in my family." God, though, replied, "But I will be with you, and you shall smite the Midianites as one man." (Judges 6:15-16 Revised Standard Version)

· The objection that the description of the Star in Matthew seems more a natural than an extradimensional phenomenon just doesn't hold up on a close reading of the text. We've spent the entire last section of this book examining the so-called natural or scientific explanations, and they all fall short. It's the very description in Matthew that directs us beyond the natural to that which transcends what we regard as natural. An object can't appear and disappear, be highly mobile and emit some sort of directional guiding light and still be a normal astronomical body.

· The argument that Matthew doesn't mention any supernatural communication from the Star to the Magi also seems weak. We already know explicitly from the second chapter of Matthew that the Magi were warned in a dream not to return to Herod after they had seen Jesus. Why shouldn't God also have used a dream or series of dreams to tell these priests that the Star, or the strange luminous body they would see, would be a sign of the coming of the Messiah in Judea? God frequently gives a revelation and then a confirming sign, and there's no reason to think He might not have done so initially when the Magi encountered the Star in their homeland.

· The fifth and final objection, that Matthew only records what the Magi thought they saw rather than what actually happened, comes dangerously close to denying that Matthew accurately described the incident.

If we play games with the text this way, then we enter a realm of speculation and fantasy that can only distract us from our final goal—the discovery of the true meaning and identity of the Star. Even though the science of Matthew's time wasn't as refined as it is today, we have to assume the description of the Star's activity is accurate. It didn't just "appear" to move, stop, and stand over where the child was—it actually did these things.

So we're definitely dealing with something extraordinary, something that might be described as "extradimensional" or "supernatural" or "miraculous," depending on which sort of terminology appeals most to you. Whichever words you use, the meaning is the same: through the Star of Bethlehem, God broke through from another level of reality into human history and announced the arrival of His Son.

But the Star story doesn't begin in Bethlehem. To understand more specifically what the Star was and what it might mean for us today, it's necessary to delve back into the most ancient Hebrew records for additional information.

As a matter of fact, one of the most familiar Old Testament incidents has some definite echoes of the Star of Bethlehem. Think back to that critical crossroads in the history of the people of Israel, when they had just left bondage under Pharaoh in Egypt and were setting out across the wilderness of the Sinai. The first Passover had just occurred, when the Lord passed over the houses of the Israelites and left all their inhabitants in safety, but killed all the firstborn, both people and animals, among the Egyptians. (See Exodus 12–13.)

The Egyptians at that point said "good riddance" to Moses and the Israelites. And the Israelites, now on their own, were heading toward the Red Sea and the wilderness beyond. They were equipped for battle, and Moses was carrying the bones of the patriarch Joseph, who had told the people of Israel many years before, "God will visit you; then you must carry my bones with you from here."

Despite these preparations and the various miracles God had performed through Moses and Aaron to convince the Pharaoh to let the Israelites go, the Hebrew people were apparently still somewhat fainthearted. God told Moses that he should avoid heading up the Mediterranean coast toward the land of the Philistines because if they went in that direction and got involved in any fighting, they might get cold feet and head back toward Egypt.

But the wilderness of the Sinai had its own dangers and discouragements, so God gave Moses and the Israelites a set of mobile, heavenly guides to assure them they were on the right track. Or, as the Bible puts it, "the Lord went before them by day in a pillar of cloud to lead them along the way, and by night in a pillar of fire to give them light, that they might travel by day and by night; the pillar of cloud by day and the pillar of fire by night did not depart from before the people." (Exodus 13:21–22 RSV)

If you make a couple of strategic alterations in this story—namely, substitute "Star" for "pillar of fire" and "the Magi" for "the people," you have an account that is strikingly similar to that in the second chapter of Matthew. The Star moved ahead of the wise men and guided them, just as did the pillars of fire and cloud. But is it possible that these two phenomena, separated by more than a thousand years in time, could be identical?

Our search has progressed to the stage where the Star of Bethlehem is about to become an *identified*, rather than an unidentified, object in the skies.

CHAPTER FOURTEEN

AN IDENTIFIED FLYING OBJECT?

The Star of Bethlehem was not an isolated, once-in-history kind of thing. Supernatural—or extradimensional—guiding lights have been a recurrent theme, both in the Old and New Testaments and even in more recent times.

These "good" extradimensional lights—as opposed to the disturbing and possibly evil UFO's—have signaled some of God's most dramatic encounters with mankind. The ancient Hebrews came to call these appearances of God the *Shekinah:* the glory, radiance, presence or merely the "dwelling" of God with His people. There was always a great immediacy and nearness in these appearances of the Shekinah, and also a spectacular quality, often characterized by some sort of un-earthly light.

The first reference to the Shekinah glory of God is found right in the beginning. In the first chapter of the Book of Genesis, you'll remember, light was created on the first day of creation, but the sources of light in the physical heavens—the sun, moon and stars—weren't created until the fourth day. So you can see that the first light couldn't have been what we would call "natural." It must have been that supernatural display of the glory of God that appears often when God reveals Himself to men.

Of course, this shouldn't be at all surprising. God's purpose in history, which is indicated again and again in the Bible, is to bring glory to Himself through His creation and especially through men and women, who are the pinnacle of His creation. There are a number of ways that God reveals His glory to us, but one of the most dramatic ways is through that brilliant and often blinding light that accompanies His presence with us.

Apparently, this light also tells us something about the extradimensional realm. The heavenly glory of God must make everything more beautiful and certainly more understandable. Of course, words such as "light" and "beautiful" and "understandable" are merely cloudy human expressions of an extradimensional reality that we can't even imagine. We do not have the intellectual capabilities to understand, but the experiences of some ordinary human beings in the Bible should give us a little clearer picture of what this Shekinah dimension is all about.

Perhaps the first recorded instance of man encountering the Shekinah glory or presence of God occurred in the Garden of Eden, just after Adam and Eve succumbed to temptation and ate the forbidden fruit offered by the serpent Satan. The Bible says in Genesis 3:8, "And they heard the sound of the Lord God walking in the garden in the cool of the day, and the man and his wife hid themselves from the presence of the Lord God among the trees of the garden." (NASB)

This incident reveals a significant thing about the Shekinah. God's presence is comforting and exciting for those who are aligned with Him and His purposes. But when we become disobedient, or begin to side with the Evil One—as Adam and Eve did with the serpent—the situation changes. The glory of God becomes a frightening thing, and the rebellious person's inclination is to run in the other direction.

More explicit connections between the Shekinah presence

of God and bright lights occurred several times in Moses' experiences with God. The first time, Moses was tending the flocks of his father-in-law, Jethro, on Mount Horeb. Suddenly, an angel of the Lord appeared to Moses in a flame of fire from a bush on the mountain—but this was a different kind of fire from anything Moses had ever seen. The bush certainly seemed to be burning, yet the flames weren't consuming it.

Moses walked over to take a closer look, and at that moment God Himself called out of the flames, "Moses, Moses! . . . Do not come near; put off your shoes from your feet, for the place on which you are standing is holy ground." (Exodus 3:4–5 RSV)

Then God identified himself clearly as the God of the great Hebrew patriarchs, and Moses hid his face because he was afraid to look directly at God.

This appearance of God in the midst of an unearthly light— some sort of supernatural or extradimensional flame which didn't consume matter in the same way our fires do—was followed immediately by a divine message.

Or, to be more accurate, what followed was an argument in which God tried to get His message across and Moses kept objecting for one reason or another. The basic message was that God had a plan to free the Israelites from Egyptian bondage, and He had chosen Moses to play a key role and would give him power to perform miracles to achieve it. But Moses kept interrupting, "Who am I, that I should go to Pharaoh and bring the Israelites out of Egypt? . . . What if they do not believe me or listen to me . . . O Lord, I have never been eloquent . . . I am slow of speech and tongue. . . . O Lord, send someone else to do it." (See Exodus 3–4 NIV)

Understandably, God got angry at this reluctance, but finally Moses gave in and the plan of freedom for the Israelites began to unfold.

This was only the first of a number of encounters Moses had with the Shekinah, or the glory of God. In fact, Moses apparently was so strongly attracted to the beauty of the light of

God's presence that he specifically asked, "Now show me your glory."

God replied, "I will cause all my goodness to pass in front of you, and I will proclaim my name, the Lord, in your presence. I will have mercy on whom I will have mercy, and I will have compassion on whom I will have compassion. But . . . you cannot see my face, for no one may see me and live."

The Lord continued: "There is a place near me where you may stand on a rock. When my glory passes by, I will put you in a cleft in the rock and cover you with my hand until I have passed by. Then I will remove my hand and you will see my back; but my face must not be seen." (Exodus 33:18–23 NIV)

This request came soon after Moses had broken the stone tablets containing the law which God had given him on Mount Sinai. Moses had destroyed this first set of tablets because he got angry when he saw the people of Israel worshiping a golden calf.

So God instructed Moses to cut two more stone tablets and go back up onto Mount Sinai, and there God engraved the Ten Commandments on the stones and showed His glory to Moses.

When Moses came down from the mountain, he wasn't aware of it, but his face was actually shining because he had been in such close contact with God's presence. Aaron and the other people of Israel were afraid to come near him because of the supernatural glow emanating from him. To calm the people down, Moses began to wear a veil over his face when he was in contact with them. But when he went in to talk to God, he removed the veil.

There are several fascinating points about this account. First of all, there was some quality about God—something about His extradimensional or supernatural presence, or what we might call His holiness—that made Him refuse to let any human being look Him directly in the "face." Many of the terms God used in talking with Moses, such as His "face" and "hand" and "back," came as close as human words can to expressing those facets of God's presence and appearance. But there was obviously something so powerful and different and perhaps even terrifying about the way God manifested Himself that He felt it necessary to lay down very specific and strict ground rules for His close encounter with Moses on Mount Sinai.

Moses, in other words, had to be protected by a cleft in a rock and also had to be "covered" by God's "hand" until He had passed by. What Moses saw was only God's "back" or only a small part of His presence, and certainly not His "face." That face-to-face encounter with God in His full glory would have been too much for any mere human, even Moses, to withstand.

Yet as overpowering, and even dangerous, as God's full presence and glory could be, Moses, having had a taste of it, wanted even more. The first time he was on Mount Sinai, the glory of the Lord "was like a devouring fire on the top of the mountain." (Exodus 24:17 RSV) There was apparently something so satisfying and comforting about the Shekinah that despite the potentially terrible force and power God wielded, His love still compelled a man like Moses to want to experience and see more and more.

And when Moses came down from the mountain the second time, the nearness and glory of God had been so intense that, in a sense, part of the Shekinah seemed to have rubbed off on him temporarily. The shining of the skin on his face was clear evidence of that.

These are rather strange accounts, aren't they? It's clear that no human being is completely capable of understanding exactly what the Shekinah involves—not Moses, nor the people of Israel, nor we from our contemporary vantage point. Our science certainly doesn't provide us with any definitive answers. The closest that we can come to explaining such phenomena is to return once again to this multidimensional hypothesis. It's as though we were two-dimensional creatures, with only width and depth, trying to understand the dimension of height which we don't have and which our senses won't allow us to perceive.

The extra dimensions of God's presence, which enter our world from that parallel universe or reality we call heaven, have something to do with a powerful radiant light that accompanies divine instructions and messages. But our language can only barely suggest what the Shekinah glory involves. A person who has actually experienced the immediate glory of God knows more than most people what it's all about. But even a specially selected human being such as Moses got only a partial view or insight.

Another facet of the Shekinah glory was revealed upon the completion of the tabernacle, the portable worship place which the Israelites used as they were wandering around in the wilderness under Moses' leadership. Just after they finished constructing the tabernacle, God's presence or "glory" filled it so dramatically that Moses wasn't even able to enter the structure. Thereafter, when the Shekinah presence of God was in the tabernacle, a cloud surrounded it and the Israelites refrained from traveling. But when the cloud rose above the tabernacle, that was a signal that the Hebrew people should pack up and get moving.

Like the original pillars of cloud and fire, this tabernacle expression of the Shekinah had a long-term impact. An extradimensional divine presence was constantly with the people, and they could view the cloud and the glow of the fire in the tabernacle as they stood at some distance from the place of worship.

The "glory of God," then—this unfathomable, unearthly light that often accompanied God's presence among men—guided the children of Israel through the wilderness, protected them from their enemies, gave them light and was the manifestation of that Presence that the Hebrew people knew was the Lord with them. This Shekinah glory appeared on a number of other occasions to the Israelites when Moses was leading them, and frequently a cloud would also be present.

The function of this cloud is not entirely clear, although, like the unnatural light itself, the cloud seems to have signified that God was manifesting Himself in our human reality. Perhaps the cloud was also necessary to shield Moses and the Israelites from the full "wattage" of the Shekinah. Witnessing a "full blast" of the divine light might be the equivalent of looking into God's face, and that was an experience that is prohibited to ordinary humans, at least in our earthly existence.

A very important part of the supernatural light in the tabernacle was the Ark of the Covenant. God had instructed Moses in the construction of the Ark during their meetings on Mount Sinai, and the function of this object was twofold. First of all, the Ark was a container for several items that had become quite sacred to the Hebrews. These included the tablets containing the Ten Commandments, which Moses had received directly from God on the mountain; a quantity of the "manna" that God had provided as food for the Israelites each day during their trek through the wilderness; and finally, the rod of Aaron, which had miraculously sprouted with buds and almonds.

The second function of the Ark was even more important, for this rectangular, carved box was built in such a way that it could serve as a base for the localized presence of God when He chose to enter our three-dimensional earthly existence. Two cherubim, or guardian angels, were fashioned over a "mercy seat" on the Ark, and when God entered the tabernacle, His glory, or luminous light and presence, would come to rest between the wings of these angels over the mercy seat.

Of course, God didn't *need* this physical point of contact for His appearances to His chosen people. But He did decide for a time to begin to focus His luminous earthly appearances on the Ark. And on at least one occasion, when the Ark was taken from Israel by the Philistines during the battle of Aphek, the Shekinah was temporarily removed from Israel.

That was truly a traumatic moment for the Israelites, and especially for their leaders, including the priest Eli, who was the mentor of the last great judge, Samuel. Eli was ninety-eight years old at the time of this defeat, and both his sons, Phinehas and Hophni, were killed during the battle. (See 1 Samuel 4:12–22.)

Eli was so shocked at the death of his sons and the capture of the Ark by the Philistines that he fell over backward from his seat and was killed when his neck was broken. The widow of Eli's son, Phinehas, gave birth immediately upon hearing all this bad news, and she named her baby "Ichabod," which means "no glory," because the Shekinah had departed from Israel with the Ark.

When the Ark was returned by the Philistines after its presence had caused disaster after disaster among them, it was brought to Kiriath-jearim, where it was placed in a house on a hill. (1 Samuel 7:1–2) Years later, King David brought the Ark from that house to a tent he prepared for it on Mount Zion in Jerusalem. (2 Samuel 6:1–17) There it remained until King Solomon, David's son, built the first temple and placed the Ark in the Holy of Holies, or the inner sanctuary. This temple in Jerusalem was an incredibly beautiful and expensive structure, with decorations in gold and other precious metals. The gold and silver alone were worth well over 100 billion dollars at today's value. But the temple's greatness was enhanced to a degree that was literally "out of this world" by the presence of the Shekinah glory, with the Ark of the Covenant in the inner sanctum.

Even though this was a permanent temple rather than a mobile tabernacle in the wilderness, the divine light shone in a similar way. As the Bible puts it in 1 Kings 8:10–11: "And it came about when the priests came from the holy place, that the cloud filled the house of the Lord, so that the priests could not stand to minister because of the cloud, for the glory of the Lord filled the house of the Lord." (NASB)

Once again, the Shekinah glory appeared with a cloud,

perhaps to shield the intensity of the heavenly light. But even then the priests in the temple were unable to bear it because the glory was so overwhelming.

The glory of God is also mentioned many times in the books of Psalms and Isaiah, and Isaiah actually speaks of a time when the Gentiles as well as the Jews will see the Shekinah on a consistent basis. But for our purposes, the most significant references to God's extradimensional light are by the prophet Ezekiel, who witnessed the Shekinah in some unusual displays of luminosity on a number of occasions.

Perhaps the most dramatic sighting of the Shekinah by Ezekiel was just before the Babylonian captivity by King Nebuchadnezzar in the sixth century B.C. First, the prophet saw God's blinding light move from the guardian angels, the cherubim, in the inner part of the temple to the threshold of the temple. There was a steady movement of this light from the innermost room, called the "most holy place" (or the Holy of Holies); then to the holy place, which was an outer room with an incense altar, a lampstand, a table with ritual bread called *shewbread,* and various gold vessels; and finally to the doorway of the temple and then out into the temple court.

The next step in Ezekiel's encounter with the Shekinah is recorded in Ezekiel 10:3–5, 18–19:

"Now the cherubim were standing on the right side of the temple when the man entered, and the cloud filled the inner court. Then the glory of the Lord went up from the cherub to the threshold of the temple, and the temple was filled with the cloud, and the court was filled with the brightness of the glory of the Lord. Moreover, the sound of the wings of the cherubim was heard as far as the outer court, like the voice of God Almighty when He speaks. . . .

"Then the glory of the Lord departed from the threshold of the temple and stood over the cherubim. When the cherubim departed, they lifted their wings and rose up from the earth in my sight with the wheels beside them; and they stood still at the entrance of the east gate of the Lord's house. And the glory of the God of Israel hovered over them." (NASB)

What a spectacular sight this must have been! Again, there are some familiar elements, such as the presence of the cloud and the mobility of the Shekinah. But there are also some new factors. This time, there are real angels, not just replicas of them over the Ark of the Covenant. These cherubim move their wings with a sound that can be heard in the outer part of the temple, and they are accompanied by a number of "wheels" (read the strange description of these wheels in Ezekiel 1:15-21).

Most significant of all, though, is the movement of the Shekinah itself. Ezekiel says the glory of God actually "hovered" over the angels. It was well up into the air and was the center of an area of intense brightness. You have probably guessed by now why this particular observation of the Shekinah is so significant for us in our search for the Star of Bethlehem. This description comes quite close to meeting the requirements of brightness and mobility of the light that guided the Magi.

But before we come to any final conclusions, let's keep following this dazzling event Ezekiel reported. The final stage of the departure of the Shekinah of God from the temple in Jerusalem, and from Israel as well, can be found in Ezekiel 11:22-23: "Then the cherubim lifted up their wings with the wheels beside them, and the glory of the God of Israel hovered over them. And the glory of the Lord went up from the midst of the city, and stood over the mountain which is east of the city." (NASB)

This means that the divine light that was hovering just outside the temple moved over to the Mount of Olives, just to the east of Jerusalem. Then it went out of sight, over the eastern horizon, and the Shekinah was not seen in Israel again in Old Testament times.

This is an intriguing account, isn't it? The glory of God, expressed as a bright, radiant light, hovers in the air outside the

Jerusalem temple, then moves to the Mount of Olives, and finally streaks out of sight into the east. These visions of Ezekiel took place early in the sixth century B.C., and nearly six hundred years passed during which the extradimensional presence and light of God were absent from Israel.

But then a new era dawned. There had been many prophecies about the coming of a Messiah, a deliverer who would not only save the Jews from their oppressions but would also bring peace to the entire world. A great sense of expectation arose, and men and women began to watch for signs of the appearance of this Savior.

Then it happened. Like the missing piece in a cosmic jigsaw puzzle, a strange new light appeared in the East in about 4 B.C. Three Persian priests—Gentiles this time, rather than Jews —saw it in the sky, and they immediately recognized the overwhelming importance of this strange and wonderful light. Somehow, perhaps through a vision or a dream such as Ezekiel had experienced, the Magi got the message that the King of the Jews, the Savior of mankind, was born.

So the intense, glorious light which God had used to signal His presence to His greatest prophets now returned after a hiatus of centuries to herald the greatest event of all: the entry of His eternal Son into our time-bound universe as the first and only God-man in human history.

The Star of Bethlehem was thus the same glory of God which had caused Moses' face to shine; which had so attracted him that he had specifically requested to see the divine light again; and which had maneuvered and "hovered" in the air before Ezekiel. The special "dwelling" light of God once again entered our three-dimensional space through some "door" from the heavenly realm. It had departed into the east, and it returned from the same direction. But this time, the spectacular radiance marked the beginning of the most decisive stage in God's plan for mankind.

It seems, then, that the mystery has been solved. The Star of Bethlehem was the Shekinah which had returned to guide and reveal the presence of the Child whose name is Immanuel, or "God with us." But even if the mystery of the Star's light has been unveiled as a kind of "identified flying object," the idea of the Star as a supernatural phenomenon isn't new. John Chrysostom, the bishop of Constantinople in the late fourth and early fifth centuries A.D., argued that "this star was not of the common sort, or rather not a star at all, as it seems at least to me, but some invisible power transformed into this appearance. . . ." He came to this conclusion because of the unusual movement of the Star; its brightness; its appearing and hiding at will; and the way it pointed out the Christ child.

Some objections have also been raised to this idea that the Star was actually the Shekinah. One problem that some scholars have pointed to is that the Magi called it a "star," even though they must have recognized how unlike an ordinary star it really was. Yet remember, the word *aster*, the Greek word for "star" used in Matthew, has a wide variety of meanings. The important requirement based on the language used is that the shining object referred to as a "star" be a single entity of some sort—and that's the way the Shekinah always seems to be described.

The two primary functions of the Shekinah glory are 1) to tell us of the presence of the Lord; and 2) to guide people as the Lord directs. The Star of Bethlehem fulfills both these functions.

The Star first "told" the Magi that God was present on earth by communicating in some fashion that the Messiah, the King of the Jews, was to be born in Judea. As a matter of fact, the prophet Isaiah foreshadowed the coming of the Shekinah when he called the coming King "Immanuel" or "God with us" about seven hundred years before Christ was born. (See Isaiah 7:14.) So it seems quite fitting that the Shekinah would be used to herald the birth of God the Son among men on earth.

The Star also fulfilled the other purpose of the Shekinah

when it guided the Magi from Jerusalem to the specific house
where the Christ child was staying. The descriptions of the
Star in the first Gospel suggest a highly localized quality to
the light. And a supernatural or extradimensional object such
as the Shekinah is the only thing which completely fits all the
data presented in Matthew 2:1–12.

But the unmasking of the identity of the Star is only the beginning of our story. The appearance of the Shekinah to the
Magi marked only the first dramatic step in a series of events
that will eventually lead to the culmination of civilization and
world history as we now know it.

CHAPTER FIFTEEN

STAR LIGHT AND LATER LIGHTS

The popular Christmas story always has two major parts. The Magi and the Star of Bethlehem are one side of the coin, and the appearance of the angel to the shepherds is the other.

But is it possible that the Magi and the shepherds saw essentially the same thing in the skies?

To answer this question, let's take a closer look at the account of the shepherd incident in the second chapter of the Gospel of Luke. Here's that passage, from Luke 2:8–20 in the New International Version:

> And there were shepherds living out in the fields nearby, keeping watch over their flocks at night. An angel of the Lord appeared to them, and the glory of the Lord shone around them, and they were terrified. But the angel said to them, "Do not be afraid. I bring you good news of great joy that will be for all the people. Today in the town of David a Savior has been born to you; he is Christ the Lord. This will be a sign to you: You will find a baby wrapped in strips of cloth and lying in a manger."

Suddenly a great company of the heavenly host appeared with the angel, praising God and saying,

"Glory to God in the highest, and on earth peace to men on whom his favor rests."

When the angels had left them and gone into heaven, the shepherds said to one another, "Let's go to Bethlehem and see this thing that has happened, which the Lord has told us about."

So they hurried off and found Mary and Joseph, and the baby, who was lying in the manger. When they had seen him, they spread the word concerning what had been told them about this child, and all who heard it were amazed at what the shepherds said to them. But Mary treasured up all these things and pondered them in her mind. The shepherds returned, glorifying and praising God for all the things they had heard and seen, which were just as they had been told.

Of course, there are many differences between this narrative and the account of the wise men, but after all, the heavenly messages were conveyed to two entirely different sets of people from different cultures. Also, the two Gospel writers choose different things to stress in their reports. Luke gives us the specifics of the original divine message to the shepherds, while Matthew doesn't include the details of the initial encounter of the Magi with the Star in his account.

But there are also many similarities between the two narratives. In both cases there was a specific revelation about the Messiah accompanied by a sign—the Star in the case of the Magi, and the heavenly host with the shepherds. Both were given directions about how to find the newborn Messiah. And both the wise men and the shepherds obeyed the message from God and hurried to find the Christ child so they could worship Him.

Most important of all, though, is the presence of some sort

of dramatic, extradimensional light. The light of the Star guided the Magi and pointed out the house of Christ in a highly unusual way. And at an apparently earlier point in time, when Jesus still lay in the manger (before they had moved to more permanent quarters in the house), the shepherds also encountered a spectacular, supernatural light. In their case, though, Luke specifically identifies that light as the "glory of God," or the Shekinah that marked God's immediate presence among men. And the reaction of the shepherds to this extradimensional light was similar to that of the Israelites in Moses' time: they were filled with fear.

Once again, there's a clear consistency between the Old and New Testament accounts of the Shekinah. The brilliant light of God's presence causes a paradoxical reaction among men: they are both drawn to it and repelled by it. There is both joy and positive excitement, and also fear and dread. The immediate presence of God's beauty and power is simply too much for the human mind and body to handle. Yet human beings who have been privileged to experience this extradimensional reality—this "taste of heaven," of the perfection and happiness that eternity with God can bring—want more of the experience. Moses actually asked to see God's glory again on Mount Sinai, even though certain strict divine precautions had to be taken to protect him from the overwhelming intensity of God's presence (such as placing him in a cleft in a rock and showing him only God's "back"). The shepherds didn't ask for more. They simply gave themselves over to unqualified praise of God for all the things He had shown them.

So the experiences of the Magi and the shepherds may indeed have been two sides of the very same coin—two manifestations of the Shekinah glory, the bright lights accompanying God's immediate presence among men.

But the activity of the Star didn't end with the nativity. Although Jesus Christ as the incarnate Son of God usually kept His own divine glory or Shekinah light veiled, He sometimes let that dramatic light break forth. One of the most dazzling

examples of the presence of the Shekinah with Jesus was
when his entire appearance was transfigured on the mountain
in front of the disciples Peter, James and John.

You'll recall that Jesus took these three followers up onto
the mountain to pray, and as He communicated with the Father, the appearance of His face changed and His clothes became "bright as a flash of lightning." Then Elijah and Moses
appeared in glorious splendor with Jesus and began talking to
Him. It seems quite appropriate that Moses was there, because he had experienced a similar shining face after his intense exposure to God's glory on Mount Sinai.

The three figures, all transfigured by the Shekinah, talked
about Jesus' coming death and the fulfillment of God's plan of
salvation for mankind. Then, Moses and Elijah started to
leave, and Peter blurted out to Jesus, "Master, it is good for
us to be here. Let us put up three shelters—one for you, one
for Moses and one for Elijah."

The Gospel indicates that Peter had no idea about what he
was saying; he had completely missed the point. And as if to
set him straight, God the Father intervened in a cloud which
enveloped the three disciples and said, "This is my Son whom
I have chosen; listen to him." Then the three disciples found
themselves alone on the mountain with Jesus.

Many of the usual elements of the Shekinah are here once
more: the bright lights and shining bodies; the cloud apparently acting to shield the humans from the full impact of
God's presence (though there is no indication in Matthew
that a cloud accompanied the Star of Bethlehem); and a
specific divine message. The Star light, in other words, had
settled on the Messiah Jesus.

But after Jesus died, arose from the dead and went to be
with the Father, the Shekinah didn't depart permanently with
Him. Instead, the appearance of the Star of Bethlehem
ushered in a new age in man's relationship with God. First of
all, Christ left the Holy Spirit to be with us as God's constantly available, powerful presence in our lives. But the dra-

matic, dazzling Shekinah also sometimes puts in an appearance as well.

One of the best known instances of the entry of this extradimensional brilliance after Jesus' ascension involved the Pharisee Saul, the most feared persecutor of the new Christian believers. He was heading toward Damascus from Jerusalem to continue his persecutions when suddenly a light brighter than the sun flashed upon him on the road at noon. Saul fell to the ground and immediately heard a voice: "Saul, Saul, why do you persecute me? It is hard for you to kick against the goads."

"Who are you, Lord?" Saul responded.

"I am Jesus, whom you are persecuting," Christ replied. "Now get up and stand on your feet. I have appeared to you to appoint you as a servant and as a witness of what you have seen of me and what I will show you. I will rescue you from your own people and from the Gentiles. I am sending you to open their eyes and turn them from darkness to light, and from the power of Satan to God, so that they may receive forgiveness of sins and a place among those who are sanctified by faith in me." (See Acts 26:12–18.)

Saul discovered he was blind after this experience, but he went on into Damascus and eventually recovered his sight and became the great missionary to the Gentiles, the Apostle Paul.

But that's another story. The key thing for our purposes is the presence of the by now well-known elements of the Shekinah glory: the bright light, the message from God, and the life-changing impact on the human who has witnessed this glory.

The Shekinah glory, then, entered human history a number of times from the extradimensional heavenly "universe" that may well parallel our own. Both the Old and New Testaments record these dramatic events, but the Shekinah isn't by any means limited to Biblical times. In fact, it's quite possible that many ordinary individuals have witnessed to one degree or another the same divine light that illuminated the Star of Bethlehem.

Psychologists and religious philosophers in the modern era, for example, have noted a phenomenon called *photisms*, or dramatic, bright lights that sometimes accompany conversions or other intense Christian spiritual experiences. Charles Finney, the nineteenth-century evangelist who later became president of Oberlin College, gives this account of his own conversion:

"All at once the glory of God shone upon and round about me in a manner almost marvelous. . . . A light perfectly ineffable shone in my soul, that almost prostrated me on the ground. . . . This light seemed like the brightness of the sun in every direction. It was too intense for the eyes. . . . I think I knew something then, by actual experience, of that light that prostrated Paul on the way to Damascus. It was surely a light such as I could not have endured long."[1]

This account, which Finney immediately connected to Paul's experience, has all the elements of the Shekinah. He was impressed right away with the thought that God was present in this light, and the nearness of the Lord in His full luminosity was almost too much for Finney to bear. Not all conversions take place this way, of course. In most cases, the decision to receive Christ is made in a much quieter and less dramatic way. But photisms do occur with enough frequency for the religious philosopher and researcher William James to have observed that they "are indeed far from uncommon."

James, in his classic *Varieties of Religious Experience*, offered this description of one person's personal conversion as an illustration:

"I had attended a series of revival services for about two weeks off and on. Had been invited to the altar several times, all the time becoming more deeply impressed, when finally I decided I must do this, or I should be lost. Realization of conversion was very vivid, like a ton's weight being lifted from my heart; a strange light which seemed to light up the whole room (for it was dark); a conscious supreme bliss which caused me to repeat 'Glory to God' for a long time. Decided to be God's child for life, and to give up my pet ambition, wealth and social position. My former habits of life hindered my growth somewhat, but I set about overcoming these systematically, and in a year my whole nature was changed, i.e., my ambitions were of a different order."[2]

The fact that this person describes the light as "strange" echoes the burning bush Moses observed on Mount Horeb, where the flame blazed in an "unnatural" or unearthly way, without consuming the foliage. The Shekinah glory certainly isn't the same as an ordinary fire or the electrically powered lights we're familiar with. But the terms "light" and "flame" and similar words are as close as we can come to giving an accurate description. The luminosity and glory that surround God's presence seem to possess almost a physical quality. Returning to our original terminology, we'd have to say it's extradimensional—a quality like our own dimensions of height, depth and width, but ultimately a quality we're incapable of reducing to human language because no words or even any human perceptions can capture it.

It's often been said that God is "omniscient, omnipotent and omnipresent"—that is, He's all-knowing, all-powerful and present everywhere. But it's impossible for the limited, finite human mind to grasp the unlimited, infinite and eternal conditions of God's deity. Or to put it another way, a three-dimensional creature can't understand or comprehend a being with more than three dimensions. We know that divine qualities are vaster than human, so we're forced to fall back on words like "supernatural," "miraculous" and "unfathomable" when God intervenes in our limited space and interrupts our time-limited lives with His timeless, eternal messages.

From the extradimensional perspective, supernatural forays into our universe become, if not wholly understandable, at least somewhat easier to accept. Or, as the Apostle Paul says, "For now we see in a mirror dimly, but then face to face; now

I know in part, but then I shall know fully, just as I also have been fully known." (1 Corinthians 13:12 NASB)

One way of paraphrasing this verse might be to say, "Now, in our three-dimensional reality, we can only vaguely understand God's glory and power. But when we're finally with Christ in heaven, we'll have entered a multidimensional realm ourselves and we'll be able to look upon God 'face to face' and understand what those extra dimensions of His are all about."

For the present, though, there seem to be many tantalizing tastes God can give us of His supernatural "universe," if that's even the right term to use for the heavenly Kingdom. For example, William James reports what may be an encounter with the divine-light dimension when he describes a spiritual renewal experience claimed by one individual.

This person said he was singing some hymns during a personal devotional at home when suddenly "there seemed to be a something sweeping into me and inflating my entire being— such a sensation as I had never experienced before. When this experience came, I seemed to be conducted around a large, capacious, well-lighted room. As I walked with my invisible conductor and looked around, a clear thought was coined in my mind, 'They [his sins] are not here, they are gone.'"[3]

Of course no one can be certain about the precise meaning or validity of another's spiritual encounters except the person himself and God. But taking this experience for what it purports to be, there are a number of similarities to contacts with the Shekinah. The incidents William James records didn't occur in Persia, or Judea, of course, and there is no mention of a "star in the east" such as the Magi saw. But this person clearly sensed the presence of God in a "well-lighted room." And there was also a definite sense of being led purposefully around the room by an "invisible conductor." The presence of God, strange lights and following God's leading—those were key elements in the encounter of the Magi with the Star. And finally, there was a clear impression in this individual's mind that all his sins had been forgiven. It was apparently a supernatural message conveyed through extraordinary channels, just as the wise men had received some sort of message to travel to Judea and then had been told by God that they shouldn't return to Herod's court.

A perception of bright lights during Christian renewal and conversion experiences is occasionally reported right up to the present day. Treena Kerr, the producer and wife of the "Galloping Gourmet" TV cook Graham Kerr, says she noticed an unusual light during her own conversion.

As she knelt and prayed to Christ with her eyes closed in a church after her baptism, she felt "this bright light [come] into my face, and I thought, 'Now they've turned up the church lights. . . .' When I opened my eyes, though, I saw this man, all in white. The smile on that face was the smile of all the love you could possibly see. I mean, just complete love of everything. The man put out his hand and touched my heart, and then he disappeared."[4]

Treena is convinced, in retrospect, that the man she saw in that church was Jesus, and she dates her relationship with Him from that dramatic encounter.

There are a number of reports of this sort, and it's impossible for any human being to identify exactly what they are in each case. But from a Biblical viewpoint it seems apparent that the light of the Star of Bethlehem cannot be limited to those nights the Magi spent under the heavens. The Shekinah glory is fully capable of shining through even today into our limited, three-dimensional, time-bound existence.

When the Star's light beams down on us, it's essentially different from our earthly lights. The Shekinah is always more intense and sometimes shines so powerfully that it inspires a complex reaction of simultaneous terror and spiritual intoxication. The sense of God's presence is always overpowering, and more often than not, there is a definite divine message that motivates men and women to take some sort of significant, life-changing action.

An encounter with the Shekinah glory is always a positive

experience for those who are obedient to God. And it always leaves the fortunate person with the sense that he has been in contact with Someone who is ultimately beneficent. But what exactly is the connection between this good divine light and the "unidentified flying objects" we discussed earlier?

These extradimensional objects or creatures keep entering our human space with some apparent purpose in mind, but what precisely is their objective? From the evidence that's available, we can certainly assume that they're ultimately up to no good. In other words, the basic source of their actions is evil. And because they have powers far beyond those possessed by humans, we can assume that the source of the negative qualities they display is superhuman and extradimensional.

This leaves us with only one possible guiding force behind the UFO's: the old master of evil, Satan himself. But, as C. S. Lewis has cautioned, don't allow the name "Satan" to conjure up images of a comical creature in red tights and a pointed tail. The realm of inquiry we're getting into is much more serious than that. Far from the amusing idea of some merely mischievous character wielding a pitchfork, we're confronting a military genius who achieves some of his most devastating victories over those who either refuse to believe he exists or dismiss him as a kind of guardian angel who has just got "a little bit of the devil" in him. Make no mistake about this fact: Satan is a very real field general who has formulated a cosmic battle plan for an extradimensional war that is even now being waged and which will inexorably lead our own earth into an all-out conflict.

CHAPTER SIXTEEN

THE IMPENDING
STAR WAR

Captain Akhelarre sat in his command post, a secure bunker on a ledge well above the battlefield, and surveyed the progress of the military engagement with great satisfaction.

His troops were winning hands down. The few visible enemy forces were surrounded and vastly outnumbered. They were holed up in small pockets of feeble resistance in the vast panorama that the captain could survey. The countryside was defenseless and open to plunder, and his forces were taking advantage of every target of opportunity. Captives and goods were being rounded up by the thousands—a tremendous victory for the elite battalion of Colonel Egbo.

In fact, Akhelarre thought this might be a good time to have the colonel fly in for an inspection of the triumph. But just as he reached for his battlefield transmitter, he caught himself. What was that just below him? It was clearly an enemy patrol on the move, and they were having some striking successes. These hostile ground forces had already recaptured three hilltops and were hard at work on a fourth. Despite the enemy's small numbers, their heavy firepower and strong air support were making all the difference. The piercing searchlights and flares that accompanied the onslaught for some reason made the captain particularly edgy, as he shrank almost involuntarily farther down into the darkness of his bunker.

It would never do to call Colonel Egbo in right now. No, first things first: the priority mission was driving that patrol back out of the area. So Captain Akhelarre looked around for Lieutenant Toppock, but the lieutenant was nowhere to be seen.

"Can't count on any of these young officers nowadays," the captain muttered as he motioned Gunnery Sergeant Hattaraick to his side.

"Gunny, take a look down there," the captain barked, pointing out the invading patrol. "See that?"

"Yes, sir," the gunnery sergeant replied.

"I want those hostiles stopped and pushed out of here—pronto! Got that?"

"Yes, sir!" the gunny said with a hurried salute. Gunnery Sergeant Hattaraick knew the captain wasn't one to fool around with, especially in a battle situation. More than one noncommissioned officer had been demoted or even court-martialed after failing to respond quickly enough to the captain's commands.

So the gunny drafted a fast set of orders and barked them down to the troops on the field. Soon, the enemy patrol was surrounded on three sides, and even though they hadn't been defeated, they were retreating slowly out of the area. The unpleasant, irritating lights that accompanied them also grew fainter.

Somewhat relieved, Captain Akhelarre looked down over the edge of his bunker and saw that things were finally under control. This might actually be a good time to call in Colonel Egbo for an inspection tour after all, he decided. The battle was clearly going in their direction again, and you could never be sure when the enemy might send in another of those specially equipped patrols to do some more damage.

As Akhelarre reached for the field phone and put his call

through to the colonel, he glanced over the side of his bunker again and studied the huge garish sign just below him: "HOT LOVE—LIVE SEX SHOW!"

Strange creatures, these humans, the captain mused . . .

On the street below a pornographic Times Square movie marquee, Timothy and Joan Johnson had just about decided the time had arrived for them to leave. They had talked to several people about their faith in Jesus Christ, and three individuals—two derelicts and a depressed-looking businessman who had been talking with a prostitute—actually had prayed on the street to receive Christ into their lives.

Tim and Joan could really feel the presence of God's Spirit enveloping them. They sensed He had been empowering them in a special way that day because so often, as they strolled through this sordid strip of New York City's Forty-second Street between Eighth Avenue and Broadway, they felt almost overwhelmed by the presence of evil. Today, though, had been different. They felt almost on fire with zeal, aglow with the power of the Spirit. They would have continued to witness about what God had done in their lives if they hadn't been put under such pressure by the three Times Square denizens who had started harassing them.

First, a half-crazed old drunk had walked up and started shouting obscenities at them. Then the hard-looking young prostitute—whose "john," or customer, had accepted Christ—had started arguing they were "bad for business." And finally, a tough-looking fellow from one of the nearby peep shows began to threaten them with violence if they didn't leave.

So they walked slowly away, disappointed that they couldn't do even more for God on this special day, but still satisfied that He had used them more effectively than ever before. Just before they departed, Tim looked up at the marquee overhead, the one that practically shouted, "HOT LOVE—LIVE SEX SHOW!" He was virtually certain that for a fleeting moment he saw a face peering over the top of the marquee, the gloomy head of a creature that seemed to resemble some sort of goat.

This imaginary scenario of Times Square may actually not

be so imaginary after all. More than one Christian walking through the streets infested with peep shows, pornographic bookstores, lewd movies and live sex shows has had the feeling that Satan and his forces are definitely in control.

In any case, spiritual warfare is certainly being waged all around us—a conflict pitting the forces of light against the forces of darkness. Satan's dark forces may not include combatants with names like "Akhelarre" (a Basque term, meaning "goat pasture," which also was used to refer to the witches' gathering or festival known as a "Sabbat"); or "Hattaraick" (a warlock burned for witchcraft at Edinburgh in 1631); or "Egbo" (an evil genius, or Satan, worshiped by a secret association in central Africa). But there's no doubt that he's present in our world and that his "captains" and "gunnery sergeants" are watching and attacking us not only from pornographic citadels, but from sedate corporate boardrooms, ordinary social gatherings and seemingly peaceful family dwellings as well.

To understand the full implications of this spiritual warfare, it's necessary to get an overview of the battle plan of both sides. This background is essential to prepare us to fulfill our proper role as human beings in the conflict, and also to help us comprehend the future role of that light that was the Star of Bethlehem.

First, let's take a look at the strategy of the "dark" side. The battle plan of the evil forces has three distinct phases: rebellion; deception during guerrilla engagements; and open warfare. Here are some of the details in each of these phases:

1. *Rebellion.* Before our three-dimensional universe even existed, there was a multidimensional universe that included, but far transcended, the very space in which we now live. We can't even begin to imagine the "super" dimensions, over and above our own height, width and depth, that characterized that universe. But one thing that we do know is that one or more of these extra dimensions involved a kind of

"light" that was really more than light as we know it on earth. The radiance of that light was so powerful that a human being from our inferior universe couldn't stand it in full force. Also, there were a comfort, joy and perfect communication that accompanied this divine "light"—a light which emanated from the very creator and founder of that superuniverse, a being or personal presence that we today call God.

Two distinct classes of beings populated this extradimensional universe. On the upper level was God—or, more precisely, the three personal manifestations of God. Paradoxically, in a way that we humans simply can't comprehend, God was one entity, yet at the same time three. God the Father was one of the three distinct beings in the Godhead, and His primary function was to serve as originator, creator and sustainer of the universe. The second manifestation of God was what we call the Word, or the Logos, or the Son. The Word's role was, among other things, to act as the agency of creation and also the vehicle of salvation for one group of God's creatures—but more about them later. The third Person who is separate yet equally God is the Spirit—a divine entity with many helping functions throughout the creation.

The other class of beings in that original superuniverse included what we call *angels*. There were many types of angels, and they didn't conform to the popular stereotype of tall men in white robes with birds' wings.

Angels, in the first place, were creatures—always keep that in mind. God made them. They didn't exist from the beginning as did the Father, the Word and the Spirit. We get a few glimpses in the Bible of just how many and varied these creatures were. For example, Isaiah 6:2 speaks of "seraphim," the six-winged angels around God's throne. Then there were the "cherubim," the creatures who guarded the Garden of Eden and also watched over God's throne in the wilderness tabernacle and the Jerusalem temple. (See Exodus 25:18–22, 37:7–9.)

The angels were also divided according to ranks, with the

archangels being the "generals," so to speak. The Bible only mentions one archangel, and that was Michael in Daniel 12:1 and a few other passages. Gabriel, who announced the Messiah's birth to Mary and John the Baptist's birth to Zechariah in Luke 1, also had an important role or "rank" among the angels, but there's no indication he was an archangel.

But there was another leading angel named Lucifer, or the "morning star," who may well have been an archangel—and might even have stood ahead of Michael in God's order of things. Lucifer was very beautiful, powerful and accomplished, but apparently he wasn't satisfied. His pride and a desire to be equal to or greater than God caused him to rebel.

The result was a great war in heaven, in which Lucifer and his angels fought against Michael and his forces. But God was ultimately supplying the "support troops" behind Michael, so Lucifer lost and was cast down with his army away from the presence of God. Today, we know Lucifer as "Satan" or "the devil" and his angels as "demons." And in a very real sense this ancient battle was a "star war" because the angels are sometimes referred to in Scripture as "stars." (See Revelation 12:4; Job 38:4-7.)

Now remember, this conflict was taking place in that extradimensional universe we've been referring to throughout this book, and even after Satan and his troops lost, they retained some of their extradimensional features. They could appear and disappear at will and certainly have been able to harass mankind in ways that no human being could do. But they also lost a key dimension to their existence—a dimension that we've focused on throughout these pages: they lost that supernatural light, the reflected Shekinah glory of God that so entranced Moses; that announced the birth of Christ; and that provides the joy and understanding that God ultimately offers those who enter obediently into His presence.

The key point is that Lucifer and his angels weren't obedient. They rebelled, and that meant they were no longer entitled to be in the presence of God and His glory. The Apostle

Peter gives one of the best descriptions of what happened: ". . . God did not spare angels when they sinned, but sent them to hell, putting them into gloomy dungeons [or "into chains of darkness"] to be held for judgment." (2 Peter 2:4 NIV)

Now, it's unclear from the Scriptures just exactly where hell is in relation to heaven. They may be in sight of one another, as you'll remember was the case in the parable of the pauper Lazarus and the rich man. There, the rich man suffering in hell saw Lazarus enjoying his existence in "Abraham's bosom." But the precise relationship between these two realms isn't entirely clear. One thing that does seem clear, though, is that both heaven and hell are in an extradimensional realm or "universe," probably parallel to or coexisting in some way with our own.

The big difference between heaven and hell, though, *is* entirely clear. While God and Michael and the good angels continue to exist in a realm bathed in radiant, warm, joyous "light," Satan and his demons have lost that dimension to their existence. The divine lights have been turned out in their extradimensional world because their fellowship with God has ceased.

But this rebellion, as cataclysmic and shattering as it must have been for the defeated forces of Lucifer, didn't end the war. The conflict goes on, but now the fighting mostly involves hit-and-run encounters and few pitched battles—and certainly no spectacular "star wars" of the sort that occurred in that extradimensional "universe" so long ago. The present phase of the war might best be called *spiritual guerrilla engagements,* in which a premium is placed on espionage and deception.

2. *Spiritual guerrilla warfare.* The present stage of the battle between the forces of dark and light began eons ago, and the setting for the conflict shifted from the extradimen-

sional realms to our own three-dimensional, time-bound universe.

Why the change of locale?

The likely answer to that question must focus on Satan himself, his personality and ambitions. He obviously wasn't satisfied just with being the leader of created beings in God's kingdom. He wanted to be number one in his own universe. But when he was defeated by Michael and the loyal angels, he must have realized he didn't have any chance against God. So he lowered his sights and decided to direct his considerable energies and powers against one of God's lesser creations, our own three-dimensional world with its human occupants.

And up to this point, Satan's new strategy has proven highly successful. His primary objective has been recruiting men and women to his cause, and his primary tactic has been deception. The Devil's activity in our universe first started in the Garden of Eden, when he assumed the form of a serpent and tricked Eve into eating the forbidden fruit. Adam quickly followed Eve's lead, and the "fallen star," Satan, was well on his way toward capturing a lot of territory that had originally belonged to God and His legions of light.

Satan's character hasn't changed at all during the years since that first deception. In fact, the Apostle John called him the deceiver of the whole world and Jesus accused him of being "a murderer from the beginning, not holding to the truth, for there is no truth in him. When he lies, he speaks his native language, for he is a liar and the father of lies." (John 8:44 NIV)

Strong words, wouldn't you say? Yet they're completely true. Satan is so brazen a deceiver that he actually tried to misuse the Bible on the three occasions he tempted Christ before He began His earthly ministry. And the deceptions continue right up to our own day. We hear pornographers trying to justify their trade by arguing for "freedom of speech and the press"; adulterers rationalizing their immorality in the name of "open marriage"; and rich people trying to salve their consciences by saying they don't help the poor because "everybody should earn his own way." Yet aren't these words just echoes of the deceptions of the Evil One?

The final body count in this guerrilla war isn't in yet, but so far there's no doubt that Satan is literally on top of the world. Even the New Testament writers recognized that he was the "prince of the power of the air" and the "ruler of this world," and the "god of this world." (Ephesians 2:1-2; John 16:11; 2 Corinthians 4:4) He holds sway among men and their affairs, and any defensive measures against him may seem like an uphill battle—especially as he throws even more elaborately deceptive battle strategies in our path to try to trip us up.

One of the most elaborate, and potentially the most effective, of those strategies involves the deep fascination contemporary men and women have with unidentified flying objects. We've discussed that phenomenon in some detail and have concluded that their ultimate source is probably extradimensional and also demonic. So that must mean that Satan is behind them.

But how, exactly, does he plan to use these UFO's in his broader battle strategy?

For one thing, despite the contrary evidence (including foul odors and mutilated animals at UFO landing sites and reports of unpleasant "abductions" by aliens), he wants people to believe that the UFO's are basically good and that they hold out the promise of contacts with extraterrestrial beings who can help us make quantum leaps in our own progress as a civilization. To inspire confidence in these strange objects in the skies, he gives them interesting and colorful lights and shapes. But the impression on those who see them isn't a total immersion in the goodness of the light, as frequently happens with the Shekinah glory. Instead, there's an enticement to be drawn further into the will of the aliens, who may promise great power or a special place of mediation to the human beings directly involved in the UFO encounters.

Gradually, through these UFO contacts and supporting concepts in such movies as *Star Wars* and *Close Encounters of the Third Kind* as well as in popular television series, the attitudes and expectations of people change. They begin to accept the idea that there are actually extraterrestrial intelligences out there who can improve their lives and probably even save the world from wars and possible nuclear destruction. These beings, many people eventually decide, must have solved all their internal problems, so they ought to be able to show us how to live peacefully together as well.

So men and women watch the skies and spend millions and even billions of dollars setting up sophisticated listening posts and space projects to hasten these encounters. Slowly but surely, we're becoming a world that is lining up and looking up at the heavens, listening for some message that will save us from the drudgery and eventual death that awaits us.

In this intense state of anticipation, what might happen if a spectacular unidentified flying object actually *did* appear and, in effect, identify itself or its crew as the savior of our world? The chances are there would be a mass movement to accept the claims of the UFO and its aliens at face value. And it wouldn't be the first time Satan has tried something like this, either. Let's see what the Bible has to say about Satan's activity.

The Evil One apparently appeared in some sort of concrete form to Eve—as a "serpent," whatever that might have meant in those early times. And he also appeared in some clear-cut way to Jesus and transported the Savior around to show Him the kingdoms of the world and the powers that would allegedly be His if only He would take the Devil's path.

So we can't rule out a physical appearance of some sort to consummate the deception that Satan has been working on us for ages. This ultimate deception is summarized in a scary way by the Apostle Paul in 2 Thessalonians 2:1–10:

"Concerning the coming of our Lord Jesus Christ and our being gathered to him, we ask you, brothers, not to become easily unsettled or alarmed by some prophecy, report or letter supposed to have come from us, saying that the day of the Lord has already come. Don't let anyone deceive you in any way, for that day will not come until the rebellion occurs and the man of lawlessness is revealed, the man doomed to destruction. He opposes and exalts himself over everything that is called God or is worshiped, and even sets himself up in God's temple, proclaiming himself to be God.

"Don't you remember that when I was with you I used to tell you these things? And now you know what is holding him back, so that he may be revealed at the proper time. For the secret power of lawlessness is already at work; but the one who now holds it back will continue to do so till he is taken out of the way. And then the lawless one will be revealed, whom the Lord Jesus will overthrow with the breath of his mouth and destroy by the splendor of his coming. The coming of the lawless one will be in accordance with the work of Satan displayed in all kinds of counterfeit miracles, signs and wonders, and in every sort of evil that deceives those who are perishing. They perish because they refused to love the truth and so be saved." (NIV)

The "counterfeit miracles, signs and wonders" that Paul talks about in this passage might well have something to do with UFO's or the current fascination with extraterrestrial intelligence (ETI). Satan, in other words, would use these "wonders" to convince people that they were evidence of ETI rather than what they would *really* be—that is, evidence of the Evil One and his deceitful activity.

And some spectacular UFO incident might well set the stage for the coming of the "lawless one" that Paul refers to—a world ruler that other writers have referred to as the "Antichrist." The Antichrist would preside over a totalitarian, worldwide governmental system whose principles would be consistent with Satan's evil purposes. (See Revelation 13.) And the demoted Lucifer's ultimate purpose is to launch a second massive war against the heavenly host and true "stars," God's angels.

3. *Open Star Warfare.* On its face the idea that a creature of God—even a creature as capable as Satan—would even attempt to usurp God's throne seems absurd. But from our limited perspective, we don't have any idea what extradimensional weapons Satan has at his disposal. Perhaps the great deceiver has deceived himself into thinking he actually has a chance to defeat God in an ultimate battle if he can only solidify his position in some way in our three-dimensional universe. Of course, it may be that Satan knows he doesn't have a chance against the forces of light in a pitched battle, and he's just trying to bluff his way into complete control of our universe. Or perhaps he knows he'll lose in the long run, but he's committed to resisting and disrupting God's purposes and man's tranquillity out of pure perversity.

Whatever his specific motivations may be, it's clear that he plans to set up this "lawless one," the world-ruling Antichrist. And this dictatorship will eventually degenerate into a cataclysmic world conflict, which will eventually draw in the extradimensional forces of darkness against the angels and the God of light.

Satan, then, is following a comprehensive, well-thought-out cosmic battle plan—but so is God.

CHAPTER SEVENTEEN

THE ARMY OF LIGHT

As the battle strategy for the forces of darkness unfolds, the armies of the light are not idle.

They are deep in the second phase of a three-pronged war plan designed to engage the Prince of Darkness in combat, put him on the defensive and, then, wipe him out in a final pitched battle.

The first part of the battle plan has already been completed. The appearance of the Star of Bethlehem—or the Shekinah presence of God—signaled the beginning of phase one. Then, events moved along swiftly. It only took about thirty-seven short years—the time that Jesus, the Messiah, lived—for that initial step to be finished. Or, as the Gospel of John says so decisively:

"This is the verdict: Light has come into the world, but men loved darkness instead of light because their deeds were evil. Everyone who does evil hates the light, and will not come into the light for fear that his deeds will be exposed. But whoever lives by the truth comes into the light, so that it may be seen plainly that what he has done has been done through God." (John 3:19–21 NIV)

When Jesus died to save mankind from the forces of darkness and then was raised from the dead and ascended back into heaven, the first part of the battle plan was finished. Men and women had been deceived and led into rebellion against God by Satan, but now God had provided a bridge for them to cross back over into His kingdom of light. All they had to do was to accept Jesus as their Redeemer from the penalty of sin, and they would become citizens of the realm of light, adopted children in the household of God.

So with Christ's sacrifice, phase two of God's battle strategy went into effect. This stage, in which we are involved even now, is a time of launching sortie after sortie, wave after wave, of attacks against the forces of Satan, which are so deeply entrenched in our three-dimensional universe. Most human beings, whether they realize it or not, are serving in the legions of the Evil One. They may not always be actively spearheading his wicked cause, but they provide invaluable logistical assistance that he needs to sustain his kingdom of darkness.

Those who are unaware of the spiritual warfare that is being waged are in a highly vulnerable position. They may aid the cause of the "Dark Lord" without knowing it. By promoting the false values of this temporal world-system, they unwittingly demote the eternal values revealed by God in Scripture.

For example, those who are "fellow travelers" with Satan may not be active gossips themselves, but they may lend a willing ear to those who thrive as rumormongers. They may not be taking money directly away from the poor in their community, but if they remain silent in the presence of those who oppress the downtrodden, they're providing Satan with highly valuable silent support.

The primary objective of the armies of light that were ushered in by the Star of Bethlehem is to recapture territory and personnel held by the dark Enemy. If a particular art form or a special career field seems to be dominated by the enemy, the idea is not just to abandon that battlefield, or to surrender out of hand. Rather, the Christian should ask the question, "Is there anything I can do personally to reclaim this particular form of drama or public relations or whatever, for God?"

Capturing people is even more important. The large majority of men and women in the world live under the power of the Prince of Darkness. He has them under the power of his evil, extradimensional realm and it's up to those in the light to take action to rescue them. God sometimes acts by Himself to capture a person for His cause, as He did with Paul on the road to Damascus. But more often, He acts through one of the human beings who are fighting in His celestial army.

The primary weapons of humans in the service of the light are truth, witness and love. An active soldier for God should look for opportunities to share the Good News about the resurrected Christ with those who have not come to know Him. That is, look for those who, even though they are in darkness, seem as though they would be willing to listen to the good news about the era ushered in by the Star. Unsheathe your weapon of truth—your knowledge of the Bible and the procedures God has established for men and women to enter His supernatural kingdom. Then pull out the fire power you have with your witness—the personal stories you can tell about concrete things God has done in your life. And finally, always employ the tactic of love when you're doing battle: in other words, treat the other individual as a true person, meet his needs whenever possible and be sensitive to his emotional reactions to the truth you're trying to communicate. If you can't seem to get the point across with one set of words or terms, try another.

In these spiritual brush wars that have been going on for the past two thousand years, there are only two sides: light and darkness. So remember: This cosmic conflict has no freelancers! A person is either for Christ or against Him. Don't allow yourself to be lulled into thinking you've found some "neutral zone"—as perhaps when you're on vacation or taking a short "sabbatical" from your church work. There is no neutral ground. Either you're committed to Christ and the forces of light by conscious choice, or you're committed to the Evil One and his dark armies, by choice or by default.

Many people today believe we're reaching the last stages of this second stage of God's battle plan. In other words, the time for brush wars and skirmishes may be fast closing, and the period of more serious conflict may be at hand. Whether this is actually true or not, only God knows. The precise timetable for the deployment of His elite troops and heaviest weapons has been set, but that piece of intelligence is top secret and known only to Him. Another way of making this point can be found in Mark 13:32–33:

"No one knows about that day or hour, not even the angels in heaven, nor the Son, but only the Father. Be on guard! Be alert! You do not know when that time will come." (NIV)

In preparation for the third and final phase of God's battle strategy, a kind of "staging area" will be established in the extradimensional universe of light. God the Father, the Son and the Holy Spirit are there. So are the good angels, led by the Archangel Michael.

But there will also be a third wave of combatants, a growing force made up of beings who are at least equal to angels and in some respects are even above them. The beings in this army are none other than human beings who were committed to Christ during their earthly lives and went on to be transformed with Him in the extradimensional realm of light after death.

Jesus, for example, said, "The people of this age marry and are given in marriage. But those who are considered worthy of taking part in that age and in the resurrection from the dead will neither marry nor be given in marriage, and they can no longer die; for they are like the angels. They are God's children, since they are children of the resurrection." (Luke 20:34–36 NIV)

The Apostle Paul even adds a certain note of superiority for resurrected humans over angels: he says, in rebuking the Christians at the church at Corinth who were getting embroiled in lawsuits with one another, "Do you not know that

God's people will judge the world? And if you are to judge the world, are you not competent to judge trivial cases? Do you not know that we will judge angels? How much more the things of this life!" (1 Corinthians 6:2–3 NIV)

Humans judging angels—it's a heady concept, isn't it? We'll at least be equal to them in many respects, and we'll even be given the responsibility of judging them! The Bible is not explicit as to just how we'll judge them, but the investment of superior responsibility and exceptional power in resurrected human beings is quite clear.

So there's a steadily building army of soon-to-be-resurrected men and women who have powers at least equal to and perhaps even beyond those of Michael and the other angels of light who defeated Lucifer in that original war of cosmic rebellion so long ago.

But what is it about these heavenly humans that will make them so different and more powerful than we are?

Their main source of strength is that they've trusted in Christ during their lives in our three-dimensional universe, and that entitles them to be empowered by Him in the eternal life and light of heaven. Part of the power that they get when they pass into God's extradimensional realm is release from the limitations of their physical bodies and tremendous versatility and strength through special celestial bodies.

In a sense, those of us who are still alive are imprisoned in our physical, earthly bodies. Many people think they're lucky if they live a long life and get to stay on earth in relatively good health for more years than their fellow humans. And when a loved one dies, there's often such tremendous grief, even among Christians, at the passing of that person. But if you read the Bible closely and believe what you read, there's more cause for rejoicing at the death of a Christian than cause for grieving. (Or at least if there is grief, it should be for those of us who remain here, in temporary separation from our loved ones.)

A brief look at the nature of the heavenly or extradimen-

sional bodies of resurrected believers should show why they
will be in better shape than we are now.

First of all, the basic model for the celestial body of a
believer is the body that Christ Himself had after His resurrection (Philippians 3:21). What was Jesus' heavenly body
like? He didn't want Mary Magdalene to touch Him when she
first saw Him near the empty tomb because, as He said, "I
have not yet returned to the Father." (John 20:17 NIV) Perhaps he was just indicating that the fellowship she and other
humans would have with Him in the future would be of a
different sort.

Whatever the nature of the change in Christ's body, it was
obviously very dramatic and comprehensive. For when He
spent time later with the disciples before His ascension, He
could do incredible things that no ordinary human could accomplish. He could appear and disappear at will. And He
could also "teleport" Himself anywhere He wished. In other
words, He could move from one location to another instan-
taneously simply by willing the movement of His heavenly
body. Examples of these powers occur in the Gospels, as when
He moved through locked doors in at least one post-
Resurrection appearance to the disciples. (John 20:19)

Also, Jesus appeared both to Mary and to two of the disciples on the road to Emmaus, but in both cases He wasn't recognized immediately. Apparently, He was able in His celestial
body to keep His actual identity secret until He chose to reveal Himself. With the disciples on the road, He was actually
engaged in eating with them before they recognized Him.
And Mary was well into a conversation with Jesus and
thought Him to be a gardener before she realized who He
was. (See Luke 24, John 20:15–16)

But even though Jesus had great, extradimensional powers
in His celestial body, He was still able to eat food (though He
didn't need it) and He was also capable of being touched
physically. Remember, for example, how the doubting disciple
Thomas actually touched Christ's nail-scarred hands and His
wounded side after the resurrection. (John 20:24–28)

During much of the forty days while Christ was on earth after His resurrection (but before His ascension), He apparently remained invisible—or perhaps He spent part or all of that time in the presence of the Father. In any case, He obviously made Himself visible only when He chose to be seen by men. His usual state while among us seems to have been invisibility. This fact suggests that even while occupying the same space that we occupy, His additional heavenly or supernatural "dimensions" put Him in a realm or multidimensional universe beyond our three-dimensional perceptions. His celestial body, then, was composed in such a way that He could enter our three-dimensional universe if He liked, but He could also move easily into that parallel, supernatural universe where God and His angels reside.

It's noteworthy, by the way, that whenever Christ appeared to human beings in His celestial body, He didn't dazzle them with His Shekinah light. The Bible tells us that now He exists "in unapproachable light" with the Father, so apparently He shielded His disciples from the full impact of His Shekinah glory, in much the same way God had to shield Moses in the cleft of the rock on Mount Sinai. It was apparently only when He wanted to make a particularly important point with a tough human subject—like the Apostle Paul on the road to Damascus—that He unleashed that extradimensional light that characterizes His eternal life with God the Father.

The point of examining Jesus' celestial body in such detail is to see what the heavenly bodies of that army of resurrected believers will be like, for 1 John 3:2 (NIV) says, "we shall be like Him." More detailed descriptions of human celestial bodies can be found in 1 Corinthians 15, Daniel 12 and in various other Old and New Testament passages. The peculiarities and powers of these celestial bodies can be summarized this way:[1]

They are perfect bodies, without disease or the possibility of death.

There's an extradimensional aspect that allows the

believer to exist in God's supernatural, light-permeated universe as well as in our more limited three-dimensional realm.

These bodies are composed of a kind of celestial or "glorified" physical substance or flesh.

They don't require sleep and never get tired, but are sustained by the power of the Holy Spirit.

They don't require food, but still can eat it.

People with celestial bodies won't marry or be given in marriage (i.e., since they don't die, there's no need to reproduce).

The body can be recognized when we choose to reveal our identities.

Those with celestial bodies can move at will, or "teleport" from place to place.

Humans with God are superior to angels in that they can judge them.

Celestial bodies will be blindingly brilliant because they'll reflect the Shekinah glory of God, that source of light that was the Star of Bethlehem. (See Revelation 1:16; Daniel 12:3)

Earthly time and space limitations will have no power over those with heavenly bodies.

Those with God will not be dragged down by the habits and weaknesses of our earthly tendency to commit sin, or be disobedient to God.

The mental and perceptual powers in those heavenly bodies will be greatly enhanced because they won't be held back by the sins and limitations of our three-dimensional, fallen universe.

Each of these heavenly bodies will be unique and individual, yet they will be linked as the harmonious "body of Christ," and Christ Himself will direct them as they prepare to launch the final assault against the forces of darkness.

The Bible says that believers who have already died and those who are still alive at some particular point in the future will be gathered together into God's extradimensional realm and given their celestial bodies at that point. In other words, there will be a resurrection of those who have committed themselves to God through the Messiah in the past, and then after that those Christians still living will be caught up into the parallel supernatural universe without ever going through death. (See 1 Thessalonians 4:15–17.)

When these events, known as the "resurrection" of deceased believers and the "rapture" or "translation" of living believers, occur, the final phase in God's cosmic battle plan will be complete. All His forces—the Father, Son, Spirit, angels and celestial humans—will be ready to strike and end the power of Satan forever.

CHAPTER EIGHTEEN

THE RETURN OF THE STAR

As the last days of world history approach, many wonderful and terrifying events will occur. No one knows the exact scenario, of course. The time and the precise course of events are known only to God.

But we've been told to remain watchful and alert and to discern the signs of the times. And we also have certain concrete prophecies in the Scriptures which can help us be on guard when the final sequence of events begins to unfold. So in light of what we *do* know, here's what *might* happen as the final days of earth draw near:

The interest in outer space and unidentified flying objects and contacting extraterrestrial intelligence becomes almost an obsession as more and more UFO's are sighted, and increasing numbers of people report "close encounters of the third kind," or direct contact with aliens. The existence of UFO's becomes not just a quirky speculation by an odd minority, but a definite conviction by the majority of the earth's people.

The general anticipation of a dramatic UFO landing of some sort increases—much as the messianic expectations did just before the appearance of the Star of Bethlehem. Then, finally, it happens. A magnificent, beautifully lighted fleet of "spaceships" lands in the middle of some highly populated community, and what seem to be alien creatures from another planet on board let it be known that they have arrived to help human beings increase their prosperity and accelerate their learning and progress. Paradise seems to be on the horizon.

But actually the "spaceships" are satanic, extradimensional beings who are only giving humans the illusion they are carrying superior, extraterrestrial aliens. Their arrival occurs at the same time as the rise of a powerful, attractive political leader in one of the major nations of the world. This leader somehow becomes connected with the aliens. Perhaps they choose him as their special mediator between themselves and the rest of the human population. And it may be that to demonstrate his special anointing and their power, they arrange for him to suffer a terrible wound that would have killed an ordinary man, yet they heal the wound and make him as good as new. It's possible, for example, that wound might have occurred during an assassination attempt on the political leader.

Then this primary political leader acquires a highly capable number two man to help him preside over his dominions on earth, and those dominions grow and grow until a kind of totalitarian system has been established over the majority of the earth. It might seem incredible for one world government to be established in light of the current balance of power among our nations. But if demonic beings entered into the affairs of the earth and upset the balance of power, this scenario would become much more plausible.

The totalitarian system that is set up is not only political but economic as well. Nobody can buy or sell goods unless he conforms to the rules of trade established by the single world ruler. The dictator's true nature, his human failings and satanic influence, start to come out. The expectations of prosperity and happiness prove counterfeit, and things start to go sour around the world.

Disagreements, then riots and finally small wars start to

break out. To make things worse, nature itself seems to turn against the new system with earthquakes and other natural disturbances. Finally, some of the most disaffected peoples marshal big armies and start to move against the world ruler and his demonic supporters. At first, they might have thought they didn't have a chance against some aliens with superhuman intelligence, but obviously the "extraterrestrial intelligences" aren't as intelligent as everybody originally thought they would be. They haven't lived up to their promises, and in fact, things are a lot worse off than they were before the spaceships came.

So armies from the north, west and east start rolling toward one another, with massive land forces, nuclear weapons, and supernatural instruments of destruction the aliens give the would-be world ruler. And the place where they converge for their final battle is the tiny nation of Israel.

If you're familiar with Biblical prophecy, you've already recognized a large part of this scenario. It's taken from Revelation 12, Matthew 24 and other sections of the Bible that deal with the last days of the earth. An "Antichrist," or "lawless one" will appear, as we saw a couple of chapters back. With the power of Satan behind him, he'll set himself up as supreme earthly ruler and will finally acquire such a feeling of self-importance that he'll actually think he's become equal to God. This Antichrist is also called "the beast" in Revelation 12, and his number two man, who is also described as a "beast" or "false prophet," executes many of the orders of the Antichrist. The Scriptures give all the details: The establishment of a worldwide economic system where people have to have a "mark" from the Antichrist to buy and sell; the terrible time of tribulation that begins during the Antichrist's rule; and the beginnings of a massive war that involves the major nations of the earth.

The only new element we've injected is the dramatic arrival of the UFO's. But that added touch could fit right in with the statement in 2 Thessalonians 2:9–12 that the arrival and as-

cendancy of the Antichrist will be accompanied by all power
and with pretended signs and wonders inspired by Satan.
Given our current crescendo of interest in extraterrestrial intelligence, what better way would there be for Satan to accomplish his purposes than by exploiting the expectations of
people about UFO's?

So, following the sequence of events that has been suggested, we find several earthly military coalitions converg-
ing for a final, decisive battle in the Middle East. It will occur
at that place in the Bible which is called "Armageddon" and
which has often been associated with the vast plain or valley
of Megiddo north of Jerusalem. (See Revelation 16:16.)

The fighting becomes so intense and destructive at this
point that it seems the earth is about to be destroyed. If you
can imagine an all-out nuclear war with the Middle East as
the focal point and then try to speculate about the outcome
for mankind, you may come close to understanding how cata-
strophic the situation could become.

But just as these human beings, with the help of Satan and
the Antichrist, are on the verge of destroying the earth, the
third and final phase of God's battle plan goes into effect.
Here's how the action might occur:

The final battle, the campaign of Armageddon reaches its
climax. The forces of the Antichrist—perhaps aided by the extradimensional weapons of Satan's army of darkness—are concentrating on achieving a swift, devastating victory over their
opponents.

But then something strange and frightening happens. An
unexplained twilight sweeps across the earth. It's as though
you were sitting in a brightly lit room and somebody suddenly
turned the dimmer switch so that you were in semidarkness.
The stars, the moon and even the sun will fade in brightness.
The prophet Zechariah describes this strange happening like
this: "And it will come about in that day that there will be no
light; the luminaries will dwindle. For it will be a unique day
which is known to the Lord, neither day nor night, but it will

come about that at evening time there will be light." (Zechariah 14:6–7 NASB) Jesus puts it a little differently in Matthew's Gospel, but the import is the same: "But immediately after the tribulation of those days the sun will be darkened, and the moon will not give its light, and the stars will fall from the sky, and the powers of the heavens will be shaken. . . ." (Matthew 24:29 NASB)

This weird twilight seems to be a kind of lull before the cosmic storm. It's possible that the forces of Satan and the Antichrist and the other world powers will be locked in mortal combat at that moment, with their troops and weapons irreversibly deployed. And at that very moment, the forces of light will strike.

As the warring factions look up into the sky, they will see a terrifying sight. A panoramic window will open on the extradimensional realm of light, and standing at the entrance to this opening into God's parallel, supernatural universe will be Jesus Christ, the "Word of God," in full battle array with all his mighty troops deployed around Him. A brilliance will surround Him such as mankind has never before seen. The Shekinah glory will radiate from Him with an overpowering light that no earthly creature can withstand. If Paul was thrown to the ground and blinded by a partial blast of that light, you can imagine the effect when all the heavenly shields and clouds are cast aside. There will be no protection for the Antichrist or Satan or the forces of darkness. Nor will any quarter be shown to those many human beings who have still failed to acknowledge Christ as the Savior of mankind.

This flashing brilliance in the heavens marks the return of the Star of Bethlehem. The first time, nearly two thousand years ago, the Star heralded the first coming of the Messiah, who would provide men and women with a way back to God. This second time, the Star will signal the second coming of the Messiah—but on this occasion, He will appear not to save, but to judge.

The Apostle John got a terrifying glimpse of this event during a vision, and he recorded what he saw in Revelation 19:11–18. Here's his account in the New International Version of the Bible:

"I saw heaven standing open and there before me was a white horse, whose rider is called Faithful and True. With justice he judges and makes war. His eyes are like blazing fire, and on his head are many crowns. He has a name written on him that no one but he himself knows. He is dressed in a robe dipped in blood, and his name is the Word of God. The armies of heaven were following him, riding on white horses and dressed in fine linen, white and clean. Out of his mouth comes a sharp sword with which to strike down the nations. 'He will rule them with an iron scepter.' He treads the winepress of the fury of the wrath of God Almighty. On his robe and on his thigh he has this name written:

"KING OF KINGS AND LORD OF LORDS.

"And I saw an angel standing in the sun, who cried in a loud voice to all the birds flying in midair, 'Come, gather together for the great supper of God, so that you may eat the flesh of kings, generals, and mighty men, of horses and their riders, and the flesh of all people, free and slave, small and great.'"

The Second Coming, in other words, will involve an unexpected flank attack from the extradimensional realm by God's army of light on the forces of darkness who are locked in battle in our three-dimensional universe. But even if Satan and the Antichrist and the other armies on earth were notified well in advance of precisely how the attack would occur, they wouldn't have a chance.

Christ will launch His assault with Michael and the angels on one side and the resurrected humans with their fantastic celestial bodies on the other. If you could sit on the sidelines and watch this battle—though that's impossible because absolutely no creature and no place can be neutral or find a safe haven—you would witness a terrifying but riveting sight. The forces of the Antichrist, including the dark armies and weapons of Satan, would turn to fight Christ and the army of light. The various rulers and nations of the earth who had been struggling against the Antichrist would join in to try to repulse this new Foe.

But this battle wouldn't involve just ordinary human weapons. The most advanced nuclear weapons and other human instruments of war could certainly be exploding all over the sky, but their effect would pale in comparison with the extradimensional armaments and combatants. Satan's UFO's would multiply and turn into the throbbing, destructive demonic creatures they really are and would hurl themselves in suicidal waves against the celestial humans and angels. The force of the light emanating from Christ would be too much for them to risk a direct assault in His direction.

The celestial humans and angels, in their miraculous, shining bodies and garments, would flash back and forth at blinding speeds. They would appear and disappear and would collide in horrible but spectacular explosions with Satan's fallen angels, who are now demons.

But as fantastic as this conflict will be, it will be over in an instant. The Antichrist and his false prophet will be captured and thrown into a dimension which the Bible calls "the fiery lake of burning sulfur." Wherever that place or universe is, you can bet it won't be pleasant. Then an angel—perhaps the Archangel Michael—will streak down from his supernatural command post in heaven and capture and bind Satan. The Evil One will then be immobilized so he can't deceive the peoples of the earth again—or at least not for another thousand years. To summarize some of the subsequent events briefly, the Bible says in Revelation 20 that Christ and His saints, or resurrected believers, will live on the earth for a thousand years—the so-called millennium. Then Satan will be loosed briefly again to deceive the world at the end of the thousand-year reign, and finally he'll be cast permanently into that same sulfurous dimension where the Antichrist and his false prophet had been thrown earlier.

The last act in this scenario is the final judgment, or the "Great White Throne" judgment, where the remaining, deceased humans, who never were obedient to God and His Son Christ, will be raised from the dead to face judgment. Then they will be sentenced to the same fate that overtook Satan and the Antichrist and the false prophet.

This final judgment will mark the end of heaven and earth as we know it. Our universe will pass away, and in its place will be what the Bible calls "a new heaven and a new earth." (Revelation 21:1 NIV) The description of this new universe, where men and women who have been obedient to God will dwell, is portrayed quite vividly in these words from the twenty-first chapter of John's Revelation:

"Then I saw a new heaven and a new earth, for the first heaven and the first earth had passed away, and there was no longer any sea. I saw the Holy City, the new Jerusalem, coming down out of heaven from God, prepared as a bride beautifully dressed for her husband. And I heard a loud voice from the throne saying, 'Now the dwelling of God is with men, and he will live with them. They will be his people, and God himself will be with them and be their God. He will wipe every tear from their eyes. There will be no more death or mourning or crying or pain, for the old order of things has passed away.'

"He who was seated on the throne said, 'I am making everything new!' Then he said, 'Write this down, for these words are trustworthy and true.' . . .

"[An angel] carried me away in the Spirit to a mountain great and high, and showed me the Holy City, Jerusalem, coming down out of heaven from God. It shone with the glory of God, and its brilliance was like that of a very precious jewel, like a jasper, clear as crystal. . . .

"I did not see a temple in the city, because the Lord God Almighty and the Lamb are its temple. The city does not need the sun or the moon to shine on it, for the glory of God gives it light, and the Lamb is its lamp. The nations will walk by its light, and the kings of the earth will bring their splendor into it. On no day will its gates ever be shut, for there will be no night there. . . ." (Revelation 21:1–5, 10, 11, 22–25 NIV)

These references to the "brilliance" and "glory of God" are the last mentions of the Shekinah glory in the Bible. And they also indicate what the ultimate role of the extradimensional light—a light that was also the Star of Bethlehem—will be.

This passage in Revelation suggests that somehow our limited, inadequate three-dimensional universe will merge into or be transformed into the extradimensional, parallel universe where God and the angels now reside. In other words, there will no longer be a split between the human world and the superhuman or supernatural world. Those who have been loyal to Christ will become permanent citizens of His incredible extradimensional kingdom. The transformed humans of this realm will have celestial bodies that won't be subject to the flaws and limitations and ultimate deterioration that plague our present physical bodies.

And even though the sun and moon and stars that give us light in our three-dimensional universe will have been long since swept away, there will be no need for them. The Shekinah glory which provided a limited, directional light to guide the Magi will burst forth in its full radiance so that there will never be darkness in the New Jerusalem.

It's very difficult to explain these concepts in human language because there simply aren't any words that can capture the beauty and excitement and profundity of this new, eternal state of existence. We have to fall back on the old "Flatland" example and say we're limited, three-dimensional creatures who can't understand in this life the full meaning of the multidimensional universe inhabited by God and His angels. Two-dimensional creatures who have only the dimensions of depth and width as do those in the "Flatland" story, can't begin to conceive of creatures like us, who also have height. Similarly, we three-dimensional creatures can't comprehend beings who have four or more dimensions. We can try to suggest what those extra dimensions are like by referring to con-

cepts like the Shekinah glory and "blinding light." But ultimately, we have to conclude, as the Apostle Paul does in 1
Corinthians 13:12, "Now we see but a poor reflection; then
we shall see face to face. Now I know in part; then I shall
know fully, even as I am fully known." (NIV)

But even if we can't understand everything at this point,
the accounts of three-dimensional and multidimensional reality in the Bible give us a considerable amount of information
that we can use to prepare for the coming cosmic conflict—a
conflict which will center on the return of Christ.

The Star of Bethlehem—which signaled the first coming of
Christ—in all likelihood wasn't some isolated three-dimensional, or "natural," phenomenon. Rather, it was part of an
ongoing set of divine interventions into our existence from a
far more complex and superior parallel universe.

Moses, Ezekiel and many others from the ancient Hebrew
nation had direct encounters with the Shekinah glory, and
their reports of their experiences were strikingly similar to the
sighting of the Star of Bethlehem by the Magi. The "doors"
between our three-dimensional universe and God's multidimensional parallel universe have swung open numerous
times throughout history and have provoked a startled, but
always life-changing response from human beings. There were
the shepherds who were informed of the birth of the Messiah
by the radiant angel and host of heaven; the Apostle Paul who
was blinded on the road to Damascus; and the nineteenth-
century evangelist Charles Finney who was dazzled by God's
light at his conversion, to name only a few.

The Star may return occasionally as individuals accept
Jesus Christ as Savior, but the most dramatic and literally
earth-shattering recurrence will far outshine anything that the
Magi witnessed over Bethlehem. All history is now pointing—
or perhaps we should say rushing—toward that final culmination of the life process on this planet. Certain wonders and
signs, such as increasing reports of UFO's, are accumulating
around us. International attention, in terms of both the world-

wide fuel crisis and military uncertainty, continues to focus on the Middle East. The world economy appears to grow increasingly fragile and subject to manipulation by speculators. Natural disasters, like earthquakes and storms, seem to multiply. The military balance between the earth's strongest nations seems more susceptible to being upset now than ever before as more smaller nations enter the "nuclear club" with nuclear weapons capabilities, and as terrorist groups show they are capable of paralyzing an entire nation for periods of time.

Where are we going? The Bible suggests that these international signals indicate we're heading directly into a massive cosmic conflict that will engage both three-dimensional and extradimensional forces.

What will trigger the countdown to doomsday? The rise of a seemingly good world leader who is actually under the power of evil, extradimensional beings.

When will all this happen? Only God the Father knows. But we have been warned to prepare as though the last days were already upon us. And the signs that He has said will herald the countdown seem to be multiplying.

So the byword that should guide all our actions should be to watch and wait and prepare for the return of the Star, for the Second Coming of the all-powerful Word of God.

AFTERWORD

HOW TO NAVIGATE BY THE STAR

The purpose in writing this book was not to produce a quasi-science fiction story or a theoretical theological thesis. We've been talking about hard reality—the actual circumstances under which we live and the outline of events which are certain to occur in the future.

Although the Star of Bethlehem may not still be shining up there in the sky, it remains a very real presence in our lives in that God is now in our midst just as He was in that light that guided the Magi so long ago. He wants to lead us much as He led the wise men. He wants us to "navigate" each day by referring constantly to the presence of His Spirit in our lives.

The big problem is that most people these days haven't learned to follow the Star. They look to other "lights" or refer to charts and maps that are foreign to God's plan for our lives. The result is that many lose their way. They wander aimlessly in the wastelands of private ambition, satisfaction of personal lust and greed, and indifference to the clear signals God sends out to us from His extradimensional realm.

Another group of people actually believe they are following the God of the Star by living fairly moral lives, or being responsible members of the community or giving lip service to the Christian beliefs and rituals drilled into them during their youth. But this is self-deception. We can't reach God by our own efforts or through our family church credentials, because He demands individual perfection, and no matter how hard we may try to live up to His standards, we always fall short.

The only way we can overcome our human limitations and stand unafraid in the intense Shekinah light is to enter that extradimensional realm where God dwells. And the door which leads into God's brilliant, parallel "universe" can only be opened by one Person—the Messiah whose work and destiny are so reflected in the Star of Bethlehem, Jesus Christ.

If you have any doubts about whether you're actually a part of God's supernatural Kingdom, or if you'd like a simple way to explain to friends how they can move beyond three-dimensional living, take a look at these three steps. They are the necessary moves you must take to reach and enter the supernatural door where Christ is waiting.

STEP ONE: *Acknowledge you fall short of God's glory and righteousness.* This shouldn't be too hard to do. Just sit down for a few moments and evaluate your thoughts, actions and personal relationships. You may decide you behaved "not too bad" or even "pretty well," but perfect? Not a chance! God, by definition, is perfect, and we, by empirical evidence, are not. The Apostle Paul puts it best in Romans 3:23 when he says, "for all have sinned and fall short of the glory of God."

STEP TWO: *Accept the fact that Jesus Christ died for you, in full payment of your sins and rebellion against God, and that He rose from the dead and now reigns in Heaven at the right hand of the Father.* You may object, "How can I accept or believe such things when they happened so long ago and I didn't see them with my own eyes?" It's easy! When you read in a history book that Julius Caesar lived more than two thousand years ago and then was murdered by Brutus, you believe

it, don't you? And when you read in the morning newspaper
that a war is breaking out in this or that part of the world,
you accept that as fact. This second step that will lead you to
God's extradimensional Kingdom is similar. A history book,
the Bible, says these things are true, so all you have to do is
make up your mind to believe them. At this stage, you're just
giving your intellectual assent.

So that you'll have some relevant Biblical passages in mind
on these points, listen to what the Apostle Paul says in 2
Corinthians 5:21: "God made him who had no sin to be sin
for us, so that in him we might become the righteousness of
God." (NIV) And in 1 Corinthians 15:3–5, 8 he reports, "For
what I received I passed on to you as of first importance: that
Christ died for our sins according to the Scriptures, that he
was buried, that he was raised on the third day according to
the Scriptures, and that he appeared to Peter and then to the
Twelve. . . . and last of all he appeared to me also, as to one
abnormally born." (NIV)

STEP THREE: *Accept the free gift of salvation which Christ is
offering you.* The first two steps are useless unless you take
the third and do something about them. This action on your
part doesn't involve any moral acts or any effort to clean up
your own life. All that is required of you is to reach out your
hand and accept Him. Another way of putting this is that you
have to receive Christ into your life or commit your life to
Him. Or, as the process is described in John 1:12: ". . . to all
who received him, to those who believed in his name, he gave
the right to become children of God." (NIV)

From the moment you take this third step, Christ and His
will become the top priorities in your life. Instead of being rebellious or separated from God, you begin to orient all your
actions and thoughts toward Him. Or, to put it another way,
you begin to navigate each day by referring to His presence
and glory, which are symbolized by the Star of Bethlehem.

When you've reached this last stage in your spiritual transformation, you'll actually move through the door that leads from this universe to God's extradimensional realm. You won't necessarily begin to see angels and the blinding Shekinah light, and you may not even feel very different. But you *are* different, and the further you progress into a knowledge of God's Kingdom, the more real and exciting it will become to you.

Jesus Himself confirmed this immediate movement from three-dimensional to multidimensional existence when He said in John 5:24, "I tell you the truth, whoever hears my word and believes him who sent me has eternal life and will not be condemned; he has crossed over from death to life." (NIV)

A problem that many people face, after they have taken these three steps, is that they become discouraged or distracted by the cares and temptations of the three-dimensional world, which is still under the control of Satan. Satan, by the way, uses the very context in which we live—the cultural values and skeptical people we encounter every day—to draw us away from God. If he can't succeed in that, he tries at least to slow down our development as creatures with a new, extradimensional reality in our lives. One of his main objectives is to make the supernatural world seem less real to us than it really is. If he can convince us that our three-dimensional world is the most important and real part of our lives and that God's supernatural kingdom isn't all that immediate or significant, then he's achieved a major victory in the spiritual war in which we are all engaged.

Here are a few ways you can make God's extradimensional realm become more real and also some tips on how you can become more adept at spiritual warfare:

Arm yourself with extradimensional weapons. After you've entered God's forces of light, you'll find you first have to put on the proper armor and buckle on the appropriate weapons before you can do combat against extradimensional forces. The best description of the armor and arms you'll need can be found in Ephesians 6:10–17. This passage of the Bible speaks pretty well for itself:

"Finally, be strong in the Lord and in his mighty power. Put on the full armor of God so that you can take your stand against the devil's schemes. For our struggle is not against flesh and blood, but against the rulers, against the authorities, against the powers of his dark world and against the spiritual forces of evil in the heavenly realms. Therefore put on the full armor of God, so that when the day of evil comes, you may be able to stand your ground, and after you have done everything, to stand. Stand firm then, with the belt of truth buckled around your waist, with the breastplate of righteousness in place, and with your feet fitted with the readiness that comes from the gospel of peace. In addition to all this, take up the shield of faith, with which you can extinguish all the flaming arrows of the evil one. Take the helmet of salvation and the sword of the Spirit, which is the word of God. And pray in the Spirit on all occasions with all kinds of prayers and requests. With this in mind, be alert and always keep on praying for all the saints." (NIV)

Let's start at the top and consider in more detail the six key instruments of spiritual combat. The *helmet of salvation* becomes yours when you establish your personal relationship with the source of your salvation, Jesus Christ. The *breastplate of righteousness* refers in part to the purpose of the war that you're about to wage—the righting of wrongs in society and the encouraging of other men to turn from their evil ways to Christ. And it also suggests a morally pure life for the Christian. In fact, a persistent pattern of immorality could indicate the offending person is *not* a Christian. (See 1 Corinthians 6:9–11; 1 John 3:6.) The *shield of faith* is your conviction of the ultimate triumph of the forces of light over the forces of darkness. You know the battle plan and you know God is capable of doing anything, no matter what Satan tries to do to stop Him. Now, just believe in the outcome of what you already know to be true!

The *belt of truth* buckled around your waist is an indication that you're on alert and ready to do battle at a moment's notice. It won't do to forget even for a moment that you're deeply involved in a cosmic spiritual struggle. Always be on guard for the surprise thrust from the enemy which could leave you reeling and even temporarily out of commission. The *sword of the Spirit, which is the word of God,* means those truths that God has delivered directly to us through His inspired Word, the Bible. If you always have an appropriate verse of Scripture at hand to bolster your own flagging defenses or to use to counter lies being spread by the Devil, you'll find you're a much more effective warrior. The *feet fitted with readiness* may refer to a willingness to get out into the world and spread the Gospel to those who are still part of the armies of darkness. Also, there's a sense of being in good spiritual shape and having the endurance to go to every length to penetrate the defenses of the foe and score a decisive victory.

Finally, this entire suit of armor and weaponry seems to be held together by the commitment to constant prayer mentioned in the final two sentences. Every spiritual weapon and defense at our disposal can be sharpened, strengthened and kept in a top state of readiness only if we are constantly in communication with the head of our army, Christ.

Learn to spot the forces of darkness. We've dealt in some detail with the ways that Satan and his troops may be trying to deceive and defeat the armies of that light which was also the Star of Bethlehem. He may be using unidentified flying objects. He's certainly present in the slums and prostitution and pornography centers of our great cities.

But he's also present, perhaps in even greater force, in places where we wouldn't expect him—exclusive country clubs, in private religious schools, in local churches and in the homes of seemingly model families. His great strength is his ability to deceive, so always look for him where you would, by nature, least expect him to be.

Above all, never allow yourself to doubt for a moment that he exists. That's one of the greatest lies of all and is a smoke screen he's managed to raise in the minds of certain theologians and pastors. For one of the best sets of arguments about how the devil works, try the entertaining yet thought-provoking presentation in C. S. Lewis' *The Screwtape Letters*.

Volunteer for front-line duty. You'll never become a top-flight spiritual fighter by sitting in a "staff job" behind a desk. Take these weapons God has given you and get out into the world and lock horns with the forces of darkness!

You may say, "But what should I do first?" Try witnessing, or talking to others about what God has done in your life. Tell them how they can enlist in the army of light, and then encourage them to commit themselves. Most people are victims of inertia. Many simply won't make a decision to accept Christ unless you ask them, "Would you like to pray right now to accept Christ into your life?"

But your effort shouldn't be limited to evangelism. It's also necessary to seek out those who are needy—who need food, or clothing, or a comforting friend—and then take concrete steps to provide them with what they lack. The Bible is quite specific about the kinds of things warriors for Christ must do for others: James says in his epistle, "Religion that God our Father accepts as pure and faultless is this: to look after orphans and widows in their distress and to keep oneself from being polluted by the world." (James 1:27 NIV) And Jesus gives a clear-cut order that those who are really in His army should care for the hungry, the thirsty, the stranger, those without clothes, the sick and the prisoner. (Matthew 25:31–46)

The main point is that you can't enter God's kingdom and then expect to sit around and enjoy the light of the Star when Christ returns. If you take that approach, the chances are you haven't really made a genuine commitment of your life, and you may well find yourself on the side of the forces of darkness when Christ once again reveals His Shekinah glory in full force.

Respect your spiritual leaders. You can't be a Lone Ranger Christian, a solitary gunslinger out on Satan's plain, picking off the forces of darkness one by one. That's not the way this conflict works. It's a war that requires a team effort, a coordinated thrust by groups of Christians who find themselves placed by God in specific locations around the world.

Your pastor in the church you attend is one of the leaders you must follow. If you find it impossible to obey him for one reason or another, then you may find you have to switch to another church. But you can't sit at home and limit yourself to watching preachers on television and assume you're really an effective member of God's army. With all its imperfections, the local church is God's chosen instrument to influence the community, sponsor refugees who come in homeless from other nations, provide educational facilities to learn the Bible and sound principles of Christian living, and make available various other support services to help the needy and enhance your spiritual development.

You may also find that you want to join or support some parachurch organization to help the poor or press for needed social reforms or carry on additional work of evangelism. But in this realm as well as in the local church, it's necessary to obey the organization leaders whom God has put in charge of each ministry.

One of the best summaries of this responsibility we have as followers of Christ can be found in Hebrews 13:17: "Obey your leaders and submit to their authority. They keep watch over you as men who must give an account. Obey them so that their work will be a joy, not a burden, for that would be of no advantage to you." (NIV)

Follow God's Navigation Chart. The "Navigation Chart," of course, is the Bible. As you've seen, the preceding tips on spiritual growth and warfare all stem directly from the Bible, and they wouldn't be as clear-cut as they are if the Bible weren't their source.

The Scriptures must be the *primary* source of spiritual authority for the Christian. All experience and knowledge must be tested against the Bible, and if there's a conflict, the Bible must control. Some recent theologians and lay people have tried to substitute their own personal experience or secular knowledge as primary spiritual authority instead of the Bible. When this happens, the forces of darkness have a devastating weapon which they can use to severely cripple certain wings of God's army. There's no longer a solid standard for doctrinal truth, personal morality or social justice. Doctrine, morality and justice become what the individual believes they are. The result is that a powerful, single-minded war effort becomes a chaotic mixture of competing views and convictions. God's offensive against Satan then bogs down, and the evil army is free to strike at will against Christ's followers.

So it's absolutely essential that God's Navigation Chart, the Bible, be accepted as the primary spiritual authority against which all experience and human knowledge are tested. This is not to say that we should make an idol of the Old and New Testaments. They are merely tools which help keep us in direct touch with the will of our top field general, the living Christ. But the Bible must be our ultimate doctrinal guide and code of personal and social conduct if we expect to become top-notch spiritual warriors.

The role of the Bible in our lives has been described most forcefully by the Apostle Paul in 2 Timothy 3:16–17: "All Scripture is God-breathed and is useful for teaching, rebuking, correcting and training in righteousness, so that the man of God may be thoroughly equipped for every good work." (NIV)

As you follow these guidelines and grow closer to Christ through prayer, Bible study and sharing with fellow believers, you will gain an increasingly sharper sense of that extradimensional, parallel universe in which God dwells. We can't know the *full* excitement and satisfaction of the Kingdom of God until we're permanently with Christ in Heaven. But we can get a fantastic preview of the glory that is to come by concentrating more on finding the will of God for our lives right now.

God has established a unique bridge between this world and the next by leaving His Spirit in our midst. But it's imperative, after we've committed our lives to Christ, to remain open and responsive as the Spirit works in us and through us. The more completely under the control of the Spirit we are, the more real and palpable the extradimensional world of the Spirit will become.

Navigating by the Star of Bethlehem, then, ultimately means bringing God's presence into our lives and finding and following His will. The seas of life can be rough and even threaten to swamp us at times, but it's comforting to know there is a true beam to guide us along the way. The Star can never become an end in itself, of course, but it will remain a steady beacon, a lighthouse in the heavens that will herald for all eternity the love that God harbors for mankind.

NOTES

CHAPTER ONE

1. *See* Arthur C. Clarke, *The Nine Billion Names of God* (New York: New American Library, 1974), pp. 235–40; Arthur C. Clarke, *Report on Planet Three and Other Speculations* (New York: Harper & Row, 1972), pp. 32–41.

CHAPTER TWO

1. Suetonius, "The Deified Vespasian," in *Suetonius,* trans. by J. C. Rolfe, Loeb Classical Library (London: William Heinemann Ltd., 1914), 4. 5.

2. Flavius Josephus, "Antiquities of the Jews" 17. 10. 4–8, and "The Jewish War" 2. 4. 1–3 in *Josephus,* trans. by H. St. J. Thackeray, Ralph Marcus, and Allen Wikgren, Loeb Classical Library (London: William Heinemann Ltd., 1926–65).

3. R. K. Harrison, notes on "frankincense" and "myrrh" in *The New Bible Dictionary,* ed. by J. D. Douglas (Grand Rapids: Wm. B. Eerdmans Publishing Company, 1962), 440–41, 856.

4. Vladas Stanka, "The Star from the East and Asoka's Wheel," *Maha-Bodhi,* 70 (1962), 394–408.

5. *Herodotus,* trans. by A. D. Godley, Loeb Classical Library (London: William Heinemann Ltd., 1921–25), 1. 101.

6. Giuseppe Ricciotti, *The Life of Christ,* trans. by Alba I.
Zizzamia (Milwaukee: The Bruce Publishing Company,
1944), 250–52; R. C. Zaehner, *The Dawn and Twilight of
Zoroastrianism* (New York: G. P. Putnam's Sons, 1961),
58–59.
7. L. C. Casartelli, "The Magi: A Footnote to Matthew
2:1," *Dublin Review,* 131 (1902), 362–79.
8. Ibid., 366–67.

CHAPTER THREE

1. Jack Finegan, *Handbook of Biblical Chronology* (Princeton: Princeton University Press, 1964), 230–32.
2. Josephus, "Antiquities," 17. 6. 4, 17. 8. 4.
3. *See* Finegan, *Handbook,* 236–38; W. M. Ramsay, *Was
Christ Born at Bethlehem?* (London: Hodder & Stoughton
Ltd., 1898), 118–31.

CHAPTER FOUR

1. F. F. Bruce, *The New Testament Documents: Are They
Reliable?* (Downers Grove, Illinois: Inter-Varsity Press, 1960).

CHAPTER SIX

1. Handel H. Brown, *When Jesus Came* (Grand Rapids:
William B. Eerdmans Publishing Company, 1963), 153–54; *see
also* Cunningham Geikie, *The Life and Words of Christ,* 2
vols. (New York: D. Appleton & Company, 1880), 1, 153–54.
2. Ibid.
3. William Barclay, *The Gospel of Matthew,* 2 vols. (Philadelphia: Westminster Press, 1956), 1, 22.
4. Joseph Addison Alexander, *The Gospel According to
Matthew* (New York: Charles Scribner, 1861), 31–32.
5. George Abell, *Exploration of the Universe* (New York:
Holt, Rinehart & Winston, 1964), 301.

6. Ibid., 308.

7. Adler Planetarium and Astronomical Museum, "The Star of Bethlehem" (planetarium Christmas program script, Chicago, 1971), 13.

CHAPTER SEVEN

1. Adler Planetarium, "The Star," 16.

2. Barclay, *The Gospel*, 17.

3. William Brown Galloway, *The Chain of Ages, Traced in Its Prominent Links by Holy Scripture* (London: Chas. J. Thyme, n.d.), 612.

4. H. C. King, *The Christmas Star* (Toronto: Royal Ontario Museum, 1970), 4.

5. David R. Fotheringham, *The Date of Easter and Other Christian Festivals* (London: Society for Promoting Christian Knowledge, 1928), 1–19.

6. Joseph A. Seiss, *The Gospel in the Stars, or Primeval Astronomy* (New York: Charles C. Cook, 1882), 442.

CHAPTER EIGHT

1. Anthony P. Stone, *A Christian Looks at Astrology* (Bombay: Jyoti Pocket Books, 1974), 60–61.

2. Kenneth Boa, *Cults, World Religions, and You* (Wheaton, Illinois: Victor Books, 1977), 119*ff*.

3. Stansbury Hagar, "What Was the Star of Bethlehem?" *Popular Astronomy*, March–June 1918, 150–59, 229–37, 323–32, 392–96.

4. King, *Christmas Star*, 6.

5. Hugh Montefiore, *Josephus and the New Testament* (London: A. R. Mowbray & Co. Ltd., 1960), 10–11.

CHAPTER NINE

1. Finegan, *Handbook*, 241.

2. Roberta J. M. Olson, "Giotto's Portrait of Halley's Comet," *Scientific American*, 240 (May 1979), 166.

3. Abell, *Exploration*, 297–98.

4. Robert S. Richardson, "The Star of Bethlehem—Fact or Myth?" *The Griffith Observer*, 22 (December 1958), 163–64.

5. Montefiore, *Josephus*, 11–14.

6. Finegan, *Handbook*, 246–48; George E. Day, "The True Date of Christ's Birthday," *Bibliotheca Sacra*, 3 (February 1846), 182–83.

7. Finegan, *Handbook*, 247; *see also* Hsi Tse-tsung, "A New Catalog of Ancient Novae," *Smithsonian Contributions to Astrophysics*, 2 (June 1958), 109–30.

8. Finegan, *Handbook*, 238–48.

CHAPTER TEN

1. Abell, *Exploration*, 441.

2. See *The New York Times*, July 18, 1978, B11.

3. A. J. Morehouse, "The Christmas Star as a Supernova in Aquila," *The Journal of the Royal Astronomical Society of Canada*, April 1978, 65–68.

4. *The New York Times*, July 18, 1978, B11.

5. Ibid.

6. H. A. Blair, "Signs of the Nativity," *Church Quarterly Review*, 160 (January–March 1959), 5.

CHAPTER ELEVEN

1. Patrick Huyghe, "UFO Files: The Untold Story," *The New York Times Magazine*, October 14, 1979, 108.

2. Ibid.

3. "UFOs: Is Science Fiction Coming True?," *SCP Journal*, August 1977, 15–16.

4. "Close Encounters with Alien Beings Are Seen as Unlikely," *The New York Times*, November 4, 1979, 12.

5. Ibid.; *SCP Journal*, 16; Carl Sagan, "UFOs: The Extra-

terrestrial and Other Hypotheses," *UFOs: A Scientific Debate, Carl Sagan and Thornton Page,* eds. (Ithaca: Cornell University Press, 1972), 268–69.

CHAPTER TWELVE

1. This illustration comes from Edwin Abbott's book *Flatland,* published in 1884, and is presented in a somewhat different format in the *SCP Journal,* ibid.

2. Barry H. Downing, *The Bible and Flying Saucers* (New York, Avon Books, 1970).

3. *SCP Journal,* 15; John Keel, *UFOs: Operation Trojan Horse* (New York: G. P. Putnam's Sons, 1970), 143.

4. *SCP Journal,* 18; A. H. Lawson, "Hypnotic Regression of Alleged CE, 3 Cases: Ambiguities on the Road to UFOs," *Flying Saucer Review,* 22: 3, 18–25.

5. *SCP Journal,* 17–19.

6. Mark Albrecht, "UFOs: The Devil's Chariots?," *Christian Life,* April 1979, 38*ff.*

CHAPTER FIFTEEN

1. William James, *The Varieties of Religious Experience* (New York: The Modern Library, 1929), 246–47.

2. Ibid., 247.

3. Ibid., 247.

4. William Proctor, *On the Trail of God* (New York: Doubleday & Co., Inc., 1977), 16.

CHAPTER SEVENTEEN

1. Kenneth Boa, *God, I Don't Understand* (Wheaton, Illinois: Victor Books, 1975), 83.

BIBLIOGRAPHY

Books, Booklets, Unpublished Theses, Planetarium Scripts

ABRAVANEL, ISAAC, *Ma'ayane ha-yeshu'ah* (Stettin, 1860).

ALFORD, HENRY, *The Greek Testament*, 6th ed., vol. 1 (Cambridge: Deighton, Bell & Co., 1868).

ALLEN, DON CAMERON, *The Star-Crossed Renaissance* (New York: Octagon Books, 1966).

The Anchor Bible, vol. 26: *Matthew* by W. F. Albright and C. S. Mann (Garden City, New York: Doubleday & Company, Inc., 1971).

ANDERSON, JOHN L., *The Messiah* (London: John Murray, 1861).

ANDREWS, SAMUEL J., *The Life of Our Lord upon the Earth* (New York: Charles Scribner's Sons, 1904).

AQUINAS, THOMAS, *Commentary on the Four Gospels Collected out of the Works of the Fathers: St. Matthew*, vol. 1 (Oxford and London: James Parker & Co., 1874).

ASIMOV, ISAAC, *Asimov's Guide to the Bible*, vol. 2 (Garden City, New York: Doubleday, 1969).

———, *The Planet That Wasn't* (New York: Avon Books, 1976).

BAILEY, ALICE A., *From Bethlehem to Calvary* (New York: Lucis Publishing Co., 1937).

BARCLAY, WILLIAM, *The Gospel of Matthew*, vol. 1 (Philadelphia: Westminster Press, 1958).

———, *Jesus as They Saw Him* (New York: Harper & Row, 1962).

BELCHER, JAMES E., *Scripture, Science and the Scientific Method* (New York: Carlton Press, 1970).

BIEDERWOLF, WILLIAM E., *The Second Coming Bible* (Grand Rapids, Michigan: Baker Book House, 1972).

BINNS, L. ELLIOTT, *The Book of Numbers* (London: Methuen & Co., 1927).

BJORNSTAD, JAMES, and JOHNSON, SHILDES, *Stars, Signs & Salvation in the Age of Aquarius* (Minneapolis: Bethany Fellowship, 1971).

BLAVATSKY, H. P., *The Secret Doctrine*, vol. 1: *Cosmogenesis* (London: Theosophical Publishing House, 1888).

BLOOMFIELD, S. T., *The Greek Testament*, vol. 1 (Philadelphia: Henry Perkins, 1848).

BOA, KENNETH, *Cults, World Religions, and You* (Wheaton, Illinois: Victor Books, 1977).

———, *God, I Don't Understand* (Wheaton, Illinois: Victor Books, 1975).

———, "The Star of Bethlehem" (master's thesis, Dallas Theological Seminary, 1972).

BROADUS, JOHN A., *Commentary on the Gospel of Matthew* (Philadelphia: American Baptist Publication Society, 1886).

BROWNE, HENRY, *A Treatise on the Chronology of the Holy Scriptures* (London: John Parker, 1844).

BULLINGER, ETHELBERT W., *The Witness of the Stars*, 3d ed. (London: Eyre & Spottiswoode, 1911).

BUNDY, WALTER E., *Jesus and the First Three Gospels* (Cambridge, Massachusetts: Harvard University Press, 1955).

BUNSEN, ERNEST DE, *The Angel-Messiah of Buddhists, Essenes, and Christians* (London: Longmans, Green & Co., 1880).

BURROWS, ERIC, *The Oracles of Jacob and Balaam* (London: Burns, Oates, and Washbourne Ltd., 1938), from the Bellarmine Series III, ed. by Edmund F. Sutcliffe.

BUSH, GEORGE, *Notes, Critical and Practical, on the Book of Numbers* (Chicago: S. C. Griggs & Co., 1858).

BUTLER, J. GLENTWORTH, *The Bible-Work, The New Testament*, vol. 1 (New York: Funk & Wagnalls, 1889).

CALVIN, JOHN, *Commentary on a Harmony of the Evangelists—Matthew, Mark, and Luke*, vol. 1, trans. by Rev. William Pringle (Edinburgh: Calvin Translation Society, 1845).

Calvin's Commentaries: A Harmony of the Gospels Matthew, Mark, and Luke, vol. 1, trans. by A. W. Morrison, ed. by David W. and Thomas F. Torrance (Edinburgh: Saint Andrew Press, 1972).

Cambridge Bible for Schools and Colleges, The Gospel According to St. Matthew, ed. by Rev. A. Carr (Cambridge: Cambridge University Press, 1905).

CARPENTER, EDWARD, *Pagan and Christian Creeds: Their Origin and Meaning* (London: George Allen & Unwin Ltd., 1920).

CARR-HARRIS, BERTHA, *The Hieroglypics of the Heavens* (Toronto: Armac Press Ltd., 1933).

CASPAR, MAX, *Kepler 1571–1630* (New York: Collier Books, 1959).

A Catholic Commentary on Holy Scripture, ed. by D. B. Orchard et al. (New York: Thomas Nelson, 1953).

The Catholic Encyclopedia, vol. 9, ed. by Charles G. Herbermann et al. (New York: Encyclopedia Press Inc., 1913).

Christmas—An American Annual of Christmas Literature and Art, vol. 43, ed. by Randolph E. Haugan (Minneapolis: Augsburg Publishing House, 1973).

The Christmas Star, Planetarium script, Alexander F. Morrison Planetarium California Academy of Sciences, Golden Gate Park, San Francisco (1970–71).

The Christmas Star, Alexander F. Morrison Planetarium, booklet no. 6 (1954, 1959), California Academy of Sciences, Golden Gate Park, San Francisco.

CLARK, GEORGE W., *Notes on the Gospel of Matthew* (New York: Sheldon & Co., 1870).

CLARKE, ARTHUR C., *Report on Planet Three and Other Speculations* (New York: Signet, 1972).

A Commentary on the New Testament, prepared by the Catholic Biblical Association (Catholic Biblical Association, 1942).

COLLYNS, RIBIN, *Did Spacemen Colonize Earth?* (London: Pelham Books, 1974).

CONYBEARE, FREDERICK CORNWALLIS, *Myth, Magic and Morals— A study of Christian Origins* (London: Watts & Co., 1910).

CONZELMANN, HANS, *History of Primitive Christianity* (New York: Abingdon Press, 1973).

COOK, F. C., *The Holy Bible,* vol. 1: *St. Matthew—St. Mark—St. Luke* (London: John Murray, 1878).

Cyclopaedia of Biblical, Theological, and Ecclesiastical Literature, prepared by the Rev. John McClintock and James Strong, vol. 9 (Grand Rapids: Baker Book House, 1970).

DANIEL-ROPS, HENRI, *Jesus and His Times* (New York: E. P. Dutton and Co., 1954).

DANIELOU, JEAN, *The Infancy Narratives* (New York: Herder & Herder, 1968).

——, *Primitive Christian Symbols* (Baltimore: Helicon Press, 1961).

DAVIDSON, D., and ALDERSMITH, H., *The Great Pyramid: Its Divine Message,* 3rd rev. ed., vol. 1 (London: Williams and Norgate, Ltd., 1926).

DAVIDSON, MARTIN, *The Heavens and Faith* (London: Watts and Co., 1936).

DEEMS, EDWARD M., *Holy-Days and Holidays* (New York: Funk & Wagnalls, 1902).

A Dictionary of Christ and the Gospels, ed. by James Hastings et al., vol. 2 (New York: Charles Scribner's Sons, 1908).

Dictionary of the Bible, ed. by James Hastings (Edinburgh: T. & T. Clan, 1924).

A Dictionary of the Bible, ed. by William Smith, vol. 3 (London: John Murray, 1863).

DIJKSTERHUIS, E. J., *The Mechanization of the World Picture* (London: Oxford University Press, 1961).

DIONE, R. L., *God Drives a Flying Saucer* (New York: Bantam, 1969).

DOANE, T. W., *Bible Myths and the Parallels in Other Religions* (New York: Truth Seeker Co., 1882).

DOWNING, BARRY H., *The Bible and Flying Saucers* (New York: J. B. Lippincott Co., 1968).

DRIVER, G. R., *The Judaean Scrolls* (Oxford: Basil Blackwell, 1965).

EDERSHEIM, ALFRED, *The Life and Times of Jesus the Messiah*, 8th ed., vol. 1 (New York: Longmans, Green & Co., 1912).

ELSLEY, HENEAGE, *Annotations on the Four Gospels and the Acts of the Apostles*, 4th ed., vol. 1 (London: R. Gilbert, 1821).

EMERSON, EDWIN, *Comet Lore: Halley's Comet in History and Astronomy* (New York: Schilling Press, 1910).

Encyclopaedia of Superstitions, Folklore, and the Occult Sciences of the World, ed. by Cora Linn Daniels and C. M. Stevans, vol. 2 (Detroit: Gale Research Co., Book Tower, 1971).

Encyclopedic Dictionary of the Bible, a trans. of A. van den Born's Bijbels Woordenboek, 2d ref. ed., 1954–57, trans. by Lousis F. Hartman (New York: McGraw-Hill, 1963).

EWING, UPTON CLARY, *The Prophet of the Dead Sea Scrolls* (New York: Philosophical Library, Inc., 1963).

The Expositor's Greek Testament, ed. by W. Robertson Nicoll, vol. 1 (New York: George H. Doran Co., n.d.).

FAHLING, ADAM, *The Life of Christ* (St. Louis: Concordia Publishing House, 1946).

FARRAR, FREDERIC W., *The Life of Christ* (New York: John B. Alden, 1874).

FILLION, L. C., *The Life of Christ*, vol. 1 (New York: B. Herder Book Co., 1946).

FINEGAN, JACK, *Handbook of Biblical Chronology* (Princeton: Princeton University Press, 1964).

Five Minutes with the Bible and Science, vol. 2, no. 1 (January 1–February 29, 1972).

"Follow the Star" by Samuel Barnes, program director, W. A. Gayle Space Transit Planetarium, Montgomery, Alabama. Based on research of Dr. Constantine Hassapis of the Eugenides Planetarium, Athens, Greece, 1975.

FOSDICK, HARRY EMERSON, *The Modern Use of the Bible* (New York: Macmillan Company, 1925).

FOTHERINGHAM, DAVID ROSS, *The Date of Easter and Other Christian Festivals* (New York: Macmillan Company, 1928).

GAER, JOSEPH, *The Lore of the New Testament* (Boston: Little, Brown & Co., 1952).

GASTER, MOSES, *The Asatir: The Samaritan Book of the "Secrets of Moses"* (London: The Royal Asiatic Society, 1927).

GAUQUELIN, MICHEL, *The Scientific Basis of Astrology* (New York: Stein and Day, 1969).

GEIKIE, CUNNINGHAM, *The Life and Words of Christ,* vol. 1 (London: Hodder & Stoughton Ltd., 1883).

GILMORE, JAMES R., and ABBOTT, LYMAN, *The Gospel Commentary* (New York: Fords, Howard & Hulbert, 1889).

GINZBERG, LOUIS, *The Legends of the Jews,* vol. 1 (Philadelphia: Jewish Publication Society of America, 1909).

GOLDSTINE, HERMAN H., *New and Full Moons 1001 B.C. to A.D 1651* (Philadelphia: American Philosophical Society, 1973).

GOODAVAGE, JOSEPH F., *The Comet Kohoutek* (New York: Pinnacle Books, 1973).

The Gospel of Barnabas, ed. by Lonsdale and Laura Ragg (Oxford: Clarendon Press, 1907).

GRAY, JAMES COMPER, *The Biblical Museum,* vol. 1 (London: Elliot Stock, 1871).

The Great Texts of the Bible, vol. 8: St. Matthew, ed. by the Rev. James Hastings (New York: Charles Scribner's Sons, 1914).

GREEN, F. W., *The Clarendon Bible: The Gospel According to St. Matthew* (Oxford: Clarendon Press, 1936).

GRESSMANN, HUGO, *The Tower of Babel* (New York: Jewish Institute of Religion Press, 1928).

GUNDRY, ROBERT HORTON, *The Use of the Old Testament in St. Matthew's Gospel* (Leiden, The Netherlands: E. J. Brill, 1967).

GUNSAULUS, FRANK W., *The Man of Galilee* (Chicago: Thompson & Hood, 1899).

HALLEY, HENRY H., *Halley's Bible Handbook* (Grand Rapids: Zondervan, 1962).

HANNEY, J. B., *Christianity: The Sources of Its Teaching and Symbolism* (London: Francis Griffiths, 1913).

HARVEY, A. E., *Companion to the New Testament* (Cambridge: Cambridge University Press, 1970).

HEINDEL, MAX, *The Rosicrucian Cosmo-Conception* (Oceanside, California: Rosicrucian Fellowship, 1931).

HELLMAN, C. DORIS, *The Comet of 1577: Its Place in the History of Astronomy* (New York: Columbia University Press, 1944).

HOLZER, HANS, *Star in the East* (New York: Pyramid, 1968).

The Homilies of St. John Chrysostom, Archbishop of Constantinople, on the Gospel of Matthew, part 1 (London: F. and J. Rivington, 1852).

HOTTES, ALFRED CARL, *1001 Christmas Facts and Fancies* (New York: A. T. De La Mare Co., Inc., 1937).

The International Standard Bible Encyclopaedia, James Orr, general ed., vol. 5 (Chicago: Howard-Severance Co., 1930).

The Interpreter's Bible, vol. 7 (New York: Abingdon Press, 1951).

IONIDES, STEPHEN A. and MARGARET L., *Stars and Men* (New York: Bobbs-Merrill Co., 1939).

Isaac Abravanel: Six Lectures, ed. by J. B. Trend and H. Loewe (Cambridge University Press, 1937).

JUNG, CARL G., *Aion,* 2d ed., trans. by R. F. C. Hull, Bollingen Series 20 (Princeton: Princeton University Press, 1968).

KELLER, WERNER, *The Bible as History* (New York: William Morrow & Co., 1956).

KING, H. C., *The Christmas Star* (Toronto, Ontario, Canada: Royal Ontario Museum, 1970).

KITTO, JOHN, *The Pictorial Bible*, vol. 4 (London: Charles Knight, 1849).

KNAPP, RICHARD S., *A Star of Wonder* (Chapel Hill, North Carolina: The Morehead Planetarium, 1967).

KNOX, RONALD, *A Commentary on the Gospels* (New York: Sheed & Ward, 1954).

KUEHN, ALVIN BOYD, *Who Is This King of Glory* (Elizabeth, New Jersey: Academy Press, 1944).

KYSELKA, WILL, and LANTERMAN, RAY, *North Star to Southern Cross* (Honolulu: University Press of Hawaii, 1976).

LANGE, JOHN PETER, *Commentary on the Holy Scriptures* (Grand Rapids: Zondervan, 1960).

LE CAMUS, E., *The Life of Christ*, vol. 1 (New York: Cathedral Library Association, 1906).

LEE, DAL, *Dictionary of Astrology* (New York: Coronet Communications, Inc., and Constellation International Publishers, 1968).

LYON, THOBURN C. LYON, *Witness in the Sky* (Chicago: Moody Press, 1961).

MACHEN, J. GRESHAM, *The Virgin Birth of Christ* (New York: Harper & Brothers, 1930).

MACKINLAY, LIEUTENANT COLONEL G., *The Magi—How They Recognized Christ's Star* (London: Hodder & Stoughton, 1907).

MAC LEOD, DAVID JOHN, *The Relationship of Matthew's Second Chapter to the Argument of the Book* (master's thesis for Dallas Theological Seminary, Dallas, Texas, 1969).

MAIER, PAUL L., *First Christmas—The True and Unfamiliar Story* (New York: Harper & Row, 1971).

MARSHALL, ROY K., *The Star of Bethlehem* (Chapel Hill: Morehead Planetarium, University of North Carolina, 1949).

The Martin Luther Christmas Book, trans. and arr. by Roland H. Bainton (Philadelphia: Westminster Press, 1948).

MAUNDER, E. WALTER, *The Astronomy of the Bible* (London: T. Sealy Clark & Co., 1908).

MC CLELLAN, JOHN BROWN, *The New Testament of Our Lord and Saviour Jesus Christ,* vol. 1: The Four Gospels (London: Macmillan & Co., 1875).

MC COMAS, E. W., *A Rational View of Jesus and Religion* (New York: John Wortele Lovell, 1880).

MC DONALD, DONALD, *Star of the Magi* (Cupertino, California: Minolta Planetarium Publication No. 1, 1971).

MC INTOSH, CHRISTOPHER, *The Astrologers and Their Creed: An Historical Outline* (New York: Frederick A. Praeger, Publishers, 1969).

MC NAMARA, MARTIN, *The New Testament and the Palestinian Targum to the Pentateuch* (Rome: Pontifical Biblical Institute, 1966).

MEYER, H. A. W., *Critical and Exegetical Handbook of the Gospel of Matthew* (Edinburgh: T. & T. Clark, 1877).

MILMAN, HENRY HART, *The History of Christianity,* vol. 1 (New York: W. J. Widdleton, 1871).

MOORE, PATRICK, *Suns, Myths, and Men* (London: Frederick Muller Ltd., 1968).

MORISON, JAMES, *A Practical Commentary on the Gospel According to St. Matthew* (London: Hodder & Stoughton Ltd., 1902).

MORISON, JOHN H., *Disquisitions and Notes on the Gospels— Matthew,* 3d ed. (Boston: American Unitarian Association, 1872).

NAST, WILLIAM, *The Gospel Records* (Cincinnati: Hitchcock & Walden, 1868).

NEANDER, AUGUST, *The Life of Jesus Christ,* 3d ed. (New York: Harper & Brothers, 1851).

NETANYAHU, B., *Don Isaac Abravanel: Statesman and Philosopher* (Philadelphia: Jewish Publication Society of America, 1968).

The New Catholic Encyclopedia, prepared by the editorial staff of the Catholic University of America, vol. 13 (New York: McGraw-Hill, 1967).

New Century Bible: The Gospel of Matthew, ed. by David
    Hill (London: Oliphants/Marshall, Morgan & Scott, 1972).

A New Commentary on Holy Scripture, ed. by Charles Gore
    et al. (London: Society for Promoting Christian Knowl-
    edge, 1928).

The New Compact Bible Dictionary, ed. by T. Alton Bryant
    (Grand Rapids: Zondervan, 1967).

New Testament Apocrypha, ed. by Wilhelm Schneemelcher,
    vol. 1 (Philadelphia: Westminster Press, 1959).

A New Testament Commentary for English Readers, ed. by
    Charles John Ellicott, vol. 1 (New York: E. P. Dutton &
    Co., n.d.).

NEWTON, THOMAS, *Dissertations on the Prophecies* (London:
    B. Blake, Bell Yard, Temple-Bar, 1828).

NORMAN, ERIC, *Gods, Demons, and UFO's* (New York: Lancer
    Books, 1970).

Olcott's Field Book of the Skies, rev. by R. Newton Mayall
    and Margaret W. Mayall, 4th ed. (New York: G. P. Put-
    nam's Sons, 1954).

OLHAUSEN, HERMANN, *Biblical Commentary on the New Testa-
    ment,* rev. by A. C. Kendrick, vol. 1 (New York: Sheldon,
    Blakeman & Co., 1856).

PANNEKOEK, A., *A History of Astronomy* (New York: Inter-
    science Publishers, 1961).

PATTERSON, JOHN, *The Star of Bethlehem: What Was It?* (Bos-
    ton: Charles Hayden Planetarium, n.d.).

PELOUBET, F. N., *The Teacher's Commentary on the Gospel Ac-
    cording to St. Matthew* (New York: Oxford University
    Press, 1901).

PICKERING, JAMES S., *1001 Questions Answered About Astron-
    omy* (New York: Dodd, Mead & Co., 1966).

Pictorial Bible Dictionary, Merrill C. Tenney, general ed.
    (Nashville: South-Western Publishing Company, 1972).

Planetarium Director's Handbook, Michael A. Bennett, ed.
    (Spitz Lab., Inc.).

The Popular and Critical Bible Encyclopaedia and Scriptural

Dictionary, ed. by the Rt. Rev. Samuel Fallows, vol. I (Howard-Severance Co., 1902).

PROCTOR, RICHARD A., *Myths and Marvels of Astronomy* (New York: Longmans, Green, & Co., 1889).

——, *The Universe of Suns* (New York: R. Worthington, 1884).

PROCTOR, WILLIAM, *The Born-Again Christian Catalog* (New York: M. Evans and Co., 1979).

——, *On the Trail of God* (New York: Doubleday & Company, Inc., 1977).

RAMM, BERNARD, *The Christian View of Science and Scripture* (Great Britain: Paternoster Press, 1964).

RAMSAY, W. M., *Was Christ Born at Bethlehem? A Study on the Credibility of St. Luke* (New York: G. P. Putnam's Sons, 1898).

RICHARDSON, ROBERT S., *The Fascinating World of Astronomy* (New York: McGraw-Hill, 1960).

RIEDINGER, P. DR. UTTO, O.S.B., *Die Heilige Schrift im Kampf der griechischen Kirche gegen die Astrologie von Origenes bis Johannes von Damaskos, Studien zur Dogmengeschicte und zur Geschicte der Astrologie* (Innsbruck: Universitäts-verlag Wagner, 1956).

ROBERTSON, A. T., *Harmony of the Gospels for Students of the Life of Christ* (New York: Harper & Row, 1950).

——, *Word Pictures in the New Testament* (New York: Harper & Brothers, 1930).

ROBINSON, JAMES HOWARD, "The Great Comet of 1680—A Study in the History of Rationalism" (Ph.D. thesis at Columbia University; Northfield, Minnesota, 1916).

ROLLESTON, FRANCES, *Mazzaroth; or, the Constellations,* part II (London: Rivingtons, 1876).

SAGAN, CARL, and PAGE, THORNTON, *UFO's—A Scientific Debate* (New York: W. W. Norton & Co., 1972).

St. Augustine—Sermons for Christmas and Epiphany, trans. and annotated by Thomas Comerford Lawler (London: Longmans, Green & Co., 1952).

SANTILLANA, GIORGIO DO, and DECHEND, HERTHA VON, *Hamlet's Mill* (Boston: Gambit, 1969).

SCHAAFFS, WERNER, *Theology, Physics, and Miracles* (Washington, D.C.: Canon Press, 1973).

SCHAFF, PHILIP, *History of the Christian Church,* vol. 1: *Apostolic Christianity A.D. 1–100* (New York: Charles Scribner's Sons, 1888).

SEISS, JOSEPH A., *The Gospel in the Stars or, Primeval Astronomy* (Philadelphia: E. Claxton & Co., 1882).

SMITH, HAROLD, *Ante-Nicene Exegesis of the Gospels,* vol. 1 (London: Society for Promoting Christian Knowledge, 1925).

SMITH, MARK, "A Fresh Approach to the Birth Narrative Events of Our Lord as Recorded in the Second Chapters of Matthew and Luke" (master's thesis, Dallas Theological Seminary, 1966).

SPENCER, H. S., *The Aryan Ecliptic Cycle* (Poona: H. P. Vaswani, 1965).

Splendour of the Heavens, ed. by Rev. T. E. R. Phillips and Dr. W. H. Stevenson (New York: Robert M. McBridge and Co., 1925).

The Star in the East (planetarium script of the USAF Academy Planetarium).

"The Star of Bethlehem," *Space Frontiers,* vol. 6, no. 3 (Chicago Planetarium Society, December 1967).

Star of Wonder or The Star of Bethlehem Show 1975 (planetarium script, Oregon Museum of Science and Industry, Portland, Oregon).

STAUFFER, ETHELBERT, *Jesus and His Story* (New York: Alfred A. Knopf, 1960).

STRAUSS, DAVID F. *The Life of Jesus Critically Examined* (Philadelphia: Fortress Press, 1972).

TALMAGE, JAMES E., *Jesus the Christ* (Salt Lake City: Deseret Book Co., 1969).

THOBURN, THOMAS JAMES, *Mythical Interpretation of the Gospels* (New York: Charles Scribner's Sons, 1916).

THOMPSON, C. J. S., *The Mystery and Romance of Astrology* (New York: Brentano's Ltd., 1971).

THORNDIKE, LYNN, *A History of Magic and Experimental Science*, vol. 1 (New York: Macmillan Company, 1923).

TRENCH, RICHARD CHENEVIX, *The Star of the Wise Men* (New York: Lane & Scott, 1851).

TUCKERMAN, BRYANT, *Planetary, Lunar and Solar Positions 601 B.C. to A.D. 1 at Five-Day and Ten-Day Intervals* (Philadelphia: American Philosophical Society, 1962).

UNGER, MERRILL F., *Unger's Bible Dictionary* (Chicago: Moody Press, 1957).

——, *Unger's Bible Handbook* (Chicago: Moody Press, 1966).

UPHAM, FRANCIS W., *Star of Our Lord* (New York: Eaton and Mains, 1901).

——, *The Wise Men: Who They Were; and How They Came to Jerusalem* (New York: Nelson and Phillips, 1973).

VALLINGS, J. F., *Jesus Christ the Divine Man* (New York: Fleming H. Revell, n.d.).

VALPY, E., *The New Testament; with English Notes*, 4th ed., vol. 1 (London: A. J. Valpy, 1836).

WARSCHAUER, J. *The Historical Life of Christ* (London: T. Fisher Unwin, Ltd., 1927).

WEDEL, THEODORE OTTO, *The Mediaeval Attitude Toward Astrology* (New Haven: Yale University Press, 1920).

WHEDON, D. D., *Commentary on the Gospels*, vol. 1: *Matthew–Mark* (New York: Nelson and Phillips, 1860).

WHELESS, JOSEPH, *Is It God's Word?* (New York: Alfred A. Knopf, 1926).

WHITBY, DANIEL, *A Paraphrase and Commentary on the New Testament*, vol. 1: *The Gospels and the Acts of the Apostles* (London: James Moyes, 1809).

WHITE, A. D., *A History of the Warfare of Science with Theology* (New York: Dover Publications, 1960).

WILLIAMS, REV. ISAAC, *The Gospel Narrative of Our Lord's Na-*

tivity Harmonized: With Reflections (London: Francis & John Rivington, 1844).

WILSON, CLIFFORD, *UFO's and Their Mission Impossible* (New York: Signet, 1974).

ZARKON, *The Zarkon Principle* (New York: Signet, 1975).

Periodicals and Articles

ANGUS, W. KENNETH, "An Early Reference to an Astronomical Event Comes to Light," *Journal of the Royal Astronomical Society of Canada,* 35 (1941).

BALLANTYNE, J. W., "The Star in the East," *The Expository Times,* 28 (March 1917).

BARRY, CATHARINE E., "The Star of the Magi," *Sky & Telescope,* 7 (December 1947).

BARTON, WILLIAM H., "Christmas Story," *Sky & Telescope,* 1 (December 1941).

BETHUNE-BAKER, J. F., "Kepler's Star," *The Expository Times,* 8 (May 1897).

"The Birth and Infancy of Jesus," *The Journal of Sacred Literature,* 2d ser. 5 (1894).

BLAIR, H. A., "The Signs of the Nativity," *The Church Quarterly Review,* 160 (January–March 1959).

BOURKE, MYLES M., "The Literary Genus of Matthew 1–2," *The Catholic Biblical Quarterly,* 22 (1960).

BRANLEY, FRANKLIN M., "The Christmas Sky," *Redbook,* 128, no. 2 (December 1966).

BRUNS, J. EDGAR, "The Magi Episode in Matthew 2," *The Catholic Biblical Quarterly,* 23 (1961).

BURKE-GAFFNEY, W., "Kepler and the Star of Bethlehem," *Journal of the Royal Astronomical Society of Canada,* 31 (December 1937).

——, "The Star of Bethlehem," *American,* 54 (December 28, 1935).

CALLENDER, GEOFFREY, "The Star of the Epiphany," *The Church Quarterly Review,* 143 (January–March 1947).

CANTON, WILLIAM, "The Nativity: An Outline," *The Expositor*, 5th ser. 9 (February 1899).

——, "The Star of the Magi," *The Expositor*, 5th ser. 9 (June 1899).

CASARTELLI, L. C., "The Magi: A Footnote to Matthew II.1," *Dublin Review*, 131 (1902).

CHANT, C. A., "Ben-Hur: The Star of Bethlehem," *Journal of the Royal Astronomical Society of Canada*, 41 (1947).

"Christmas Fact & Fancy," *Time*, 82 (December 20, 1963).

COLES, ROBERT R., "The Christmas Star," *Sky & Telescope*, 5 (December 1945).

"Christmas Star," *Science Digest*, 34 (December 1953).

"The Christmas Star," *The Griffith Observer*, 4, no. 12 (December 1940).

"The Christmas Star," *The Griffith Observer*, 15, no. 12 (December 1951).

"The Christmas Star," *The Pointer*, a periodical newsletter, Spitz Laboratories Inc., Winter Solstice, 1963 (Yorklyn, Delaware).

CLARKE, ARTHUR C., "Does the Star of Bethlehem Still Shine?" *Reader's Digest*, 66 (January 1955).

——, "What Star Was This?" *Saturday Evening Post*, 248 (December 1976).

——, "What Was the Star of Bethlehem?" *Holiday*, 16 (December 1954).

CLEMINSHAW, C. H., "The Date of the Birth of Christ," *The Griffith Observer*, 30 (December 1966).

COLE, D. I., "The Star of Bethlehem," *Monthly Notes of the Astronomical Society of Southern Africa*, 23 (1964).

COPELAND, LELAND S., "The Starry Heavens in December," *Sky & Telescope*, 2 (December 1942).

"The Criticism of the Synoptic Gospels—Their Historical Value. III," *Church Quarterly Review*, 58 (1904).

DARROW, CLARENCE, "Absurdities of the Bible," *The Humanist*, 35 (September/October 1975).

DUPONT-SOMMER, ANDRÉ, "Deux Documents Horoscopiques Esseniens Decouverts à Qoumran. Près de la Mer Morte,"

Comptes Rendus de l'Academie des Inscriptions et Belles-Lettres (June 1965).

DERRETT, J. DUNCAN M., "Further Light on the Narratives of the Nativity," *Novum Testamentum,* 17 (April 1975).

EDKINS, JOSEPH, "The Star in the East," *The Expository Times,* 8 (September 1897).

ENSLIN, MORTON S., "The Christian Stories of the Nativity," *Journal of Biblical Literature,* 59 (1940).

ETZ, DONALD V., "Comets in the Bible," *Christianity Today,* 18 (December 21, 1973).

EWING, ANN, "Star of Bethlehem," *Science News Letter,* 80 (December 9, 1961).

FEDERER, C. A., "Rambling Through December Skies," *Sky & Telescope,* 36 (December 1968).

FILAS, FRANCIS L., "The Star of the Magi," *Irish Ecclesiastical Record,* 85 (June 1956).

FITZPATRICK, JESSE A., "Venus as the Christmas Star," *Sky & Telescope,* 1 (December 1941).

FOTHERINGHAM, J. K., "The Star of Bethlehem," *The Journal of Theological Studies,* 10 (1908).

FREEMAN, A., "The Star of Bethlehem," *The Observatory,* 11 (1888).

GEMSER, B., "Der Stern aus Jakob," *Zeitschrift Astronomische Wissenschaft,* 43 (1925).

GENIMUS, "It seems to Me," *The New Scientist,* 1 (December 27, 1956).

GERHARDT, OSWALD, *Der Stern des Messias* (Leipzig: Deichertsche Verlagsbuch, 1922), a review by J. K. Fotheringham in *The Journal of Theological Studies,* 24 (1922).

GINGERICH, OWEN, "More on the Star of Bethlehem," *Harvard Magazine,* 78, no. 1 (September 1975).

GOODMAN, F. W., "Sources of the First Two Chapters in Matthew and Luke," *The Church Quarterly Review,* 162 (1961).

GOSSNER, SIMONE DARO, "The Star of Bethlehem," *Nature,* 50 (December 1957).

GUYOT, GILMORE H., "The Prophecy of Balaam," *The Catholic Biblical Quarterly*, 2 (1940).

HAGAR, STANSBURG, "What was the Star of Bethlehem?" *Popular Astronomy*, 26 (1918).

HART, J. M., "The Adoration of the Magi," *The Nation*, 96 (March 13, 1913).

HERRICK, SAMUEL, JR., "The Jupiter-Saturn Triple Conjunction," leaflet of the Astronomical Society of the Pacific, 3, no. 144 (February 1941).

HILL, DAVE, "The Star of the East," *St. Anthony Messenger*, 71 (January 1964).

"History of our Lord Jesus Christ, from the Time of His Birth to the Commencement of His Mission," *The Journal of Sacred Literature*, 13 (1861).

HOUDOUS, EDWARD J., "The Gospel of the Epiphany," *The Catholic Biblical Quarterly*, 6 (1944).

HUGHES, DAVID W., "The Star of Bethlehem," *Nature*, 264, no. 5586 (December 9, 1976).

HUJER, KAREL, "Christmas and the Stars," *Michigan Education Journal* (December 1944).

HUMBARD, REX, "The Star of Jesus," *The Answer* (December 1974).

HUNTER, S. C., "The Star of Bethlehem," *Popular Astronomy*, 26 (1918).

"The Incarnation," *The Journal of Sacred Literature*, 3d ser. 3 (1856).

JACOBS, GABRIELLE MARIE, "The Magi and their Quest," *The Chautauquan*, 36 (December 1902).

KAEMPFFERT, WALDEMAR, "Was the Star of Bethlehem a Comet?," *Cosmopolitan*, 48 (January 1910).

KANAEL, BARUCH, "Ancient Jewish Coins and Their Historical Importance," *The Biblical Archaeologist*, 26, no. 2 (1963).

LAUTH, D., "On the Date of the Nativity," *Trans. Soc. Biblical Archaeology*, 4 (1875).

LEWIS, AGNES SMITH, "The Star of Bethlehem," *The Expository Times*, 19 (December 1907).

LEWIS, ISABEL M., "Lo, the Star, Which They Saw in the East . . . ," *Nature*, 31 (December 1938).

LINDSAY, GORDON, "The Star and the Wisemen," *Christ for the Nations* (December 1974).

LITTLE, EDWARD S., "Interpretations of the Star of Bethlehem," leaflet of the Astronomical Society of the Pacific, 10, no. 474 (December 1968).

LOCKWOOD, MARIAN, "That Christmas Star," *Sky & Telescope*, 2 (December 1942).

———, "The Wise Men's Star," *Sky & Telescope*, 3 (December 1943).

LUNDMARK, KNUT, "The Messianic Ideas and Their Astronomical Background," *Actes du VII Congrès International de l'Histoire des Sciences, Jerusalem* (1953).

———, "Suspected New Stars Recorded in Old Chronicles and Among Recent Meridian Observations," *P.A.S.P.*, 33 (October 1921).

LUTHER, WILLIAM, "The Constellation of Bethlehem," *The Observatory*, 32 (1909).

MACDONALD, THOMAS L., "Beza's Verses on Tycho's Nova," *Journal of the Royal Astronomical Society of Canada*, 35 (1941).

MACLAGAN, P. J., "The Star of Bethlehem," *The Expository Times*, 19 (April 1908).

MANN, C. S., "Epiphany—Wise Men or Charlatans?" *Theology*, 61 (1958).

MARSH-EDWARDS, J. C., "The Magi in Tradition and Art," *Irish Ecclesiastical Record*, 85 (January 1956).

MARSHALL, ROY K., "Astronomical Anecdotes: Star of Bethlehem?," 3 (December 1943).

MARTIN, ERNEST L., "The Celestial Pageantry Dating Christ's Birth," *Christianity Today*, 21 (December 3, 1976).

"Maurolyco's 'Lost' Essay on the New Star of 1572," translated, transcribed and ed. by C. Coris Hellman, *Isis*, 51 (1960).

MC CASLAND, S. V., "Portents in Josephus and in the Gospels," *Journal of Biblical Literature*, 51 (1932).

MC CLELLAN, WILLIAM H., "Homiletical Notes on the Magi: Gospel for the Feast of the Epiphany," *The Catholic Biblical Quarterly*, 1 (1939).

MC NAMARA, M., "Were the Magi Essenes?" *Irish Ecclesiastical Record* (December 1968).

MEYER, H. A. W., "Commentary on the Second and Third Chapters of the Gospel of Matthew," trans. from the German by B. B. Edwards, *Bibliotheca Sacra*, 8 (1851).

MEYER, EARL R., "The Christmas Star," *The Physics Teacher*, 15 (December 1977).

MONCK, W. H. S., "The Star of Bethlehem," *The Observatory*, 32 (1909).

MONTEFIORE, H. W., "Josephus and the New Testament," *Novum Testamentum*, 4 (December 1960).

MOORE, DAVID L., "Skywatchers' Guide for December: The Star of Bethlehem Visible This Christmas," *National Geographic News Bulletin* (December 4, 1970).

MOREHOUSE, A. J., "The Christmas Star as a Supernova in Aquila," *Journal of the Royal Astronomical Society of Canada*, 72 (1978).

MOULTON, JAMES HOPE, "It Is His Angel," *The Journal of Theological Studies*, 3 (1902).

———, "Zoroastrian Influences on Judaism," *The Expository Times*, 9 (1897–98).

MURPHY, FRANCIS X., "The Date of Christ's Birth: Present State of the Question," *The Catholic Historical Review*, 29 (October 1943).

NOTZ, WILLIAM, "The Star of Bethlehem and the Magi," *Bibliotheca Sacra*, 73 (1916).

OLMSTEAD, A. T., "The Chronology of Jesus' Life," *Anglican Theological Review*, 24 (January 1942).

"On the Date of the Nativity," *The Journal of Sacred Literature*, 2d ser. 7 (1855).

OPIK, E., "The Cosmic Frame of Biological Evolution," *Irish Astronomical Journal*, 6 (December 1963).

ORITI, RONALD A., "The Star of Bethlehem," *The Griffith Observer*, 39 (December 1975).

"Parade of the Planets," *The Gospel Truth*, 15, no. 1 (December 1974).

PAYNE, WILLIAM W., "The Star of Bethlehem," *The Sidereal Messenger*, 4 (1885).

PEATTIE, DONALD C., "The Star of Stars," *Good Housekeeping*, 137 (December 1953).

PRITCHARD, C., "On the Conjunctions of the Planets Jupiter and Saturn in the Years B.C. 7, B.C. 66 and A.D. 54," *Monthly Notes of the Royal Astronomical Society*, 16 (July 11, 1856).

"Rambling Through December Skies," *Sky & Telescope*, 36 (December 1968).

"Report of the Ordinary General Meeting," *Journal of the British Astronomical Society*, 58 (August 1948).

RICHARDS, CARL P., "The Star of Bethlehem," *Sky & Telescope*, 16, no. 6 (April 1957).

RICHARDSON, R. S., "Is That Star the 'Star of Bethlehem'?" leaflet of the Astronomical Society of the Pacific, 3, no. 106 (December 1937).

——, "The Star of Bethlehem—Fact or Myth?," *The Griffith Observer*, 22, no. 12 (December 1958).

——, "What Was the Star of Bethlehem?" *Popular Science*, 177 (December 1960).

ROBBINS, R. D. C., "The Character and Prophecies of Balaam," *Bibliotheca Sacra*, 3, 347–78 (1846).

RODMAN, ROBERT, "A Linguistic Note on the Christmas Star," *The Griffith Observer*, 40, no. 12 (December 1976).

ROQUES, PAUL E., "The True Anno Domini?," *The Griffith Observer*, 35 (1971).

ROSENBERG, ROY A., "The 'Star of the Messiah' Reconsidered," *Biblica*, 53 (1972).

ROTH, CHARLES O., JR., ". . . and, lo, the Star," *Yankee*, 38, no. 12 (December 1974).

SCHAUMBERGER, P. IOHANNES, "Textus Cuneiformis de Stella Magorum?," *Biblica*, 6 (1925).

SEARLE, GEORGE M., "The Star of Bethlehem," *Catholic World*, 47 (April 1888).

SELWYN, E. C., "The Feast of Tabernacles, Epiphany, and Baptism," *The Journal of Theological Studies*, 13 (1912).

SINNOTT, ROGER W., "Thoughts on the Star of Bethlehem," *Sky & Telescope*, 36 (December 1968).

SMITH, CHARLES STEWART, "The Star of the Magi. The Epiphany Star," *The Church Quarterly Review*, 114 (July 1932).

SMITH, F. HAROLD, "The Sutta and the Gospel: An Inquiry into the Relationship Between the Accounts of the Supernatural Births of Buddha and Christ," *The Church Quarterly Review*, 92 (1921).

SMYTH, C. PIAZZI, "The Star of Bethlehem," *Good Words*, 29 (1888).

STANKA, VLADAS, "The Star from the East and Asoka's Wheel," *Maha-Bodhi*, 70 (1962).

"The Star of Bethlehem," *English Mechanic and World of Science*, 57, no. 1459 (1893).

"The Star of Bethlehem," *Nature*, 37 (December 22, 1887).

"The Star of Bethlehem," *Nature*, 37 (January 5, 1888).

"The Star of Bethlehem," *Nature*, 47 (December 22, 1892).

"Star of Bethlehem," *The Sidereal Messenger*, 6 (1887).

The Star of Bethlehem (planetarium show for December, Adler Planetarium and Astronomical Museum, Chicago, Illinois, stock no. 711).

"Star of Bethlehem," from "Word Keys Which Unlock Scripture," as analyzed by Duane Edward Spencer, Grace Bible Church ("Word of Grace" radio broadcast, WOAI, San Antonio, Texas).

"Star of Bethlehem May Be Visible This Christmas," *Kitt Peak Skywatcher* (Kitt Peak National Observatory, Tucson, Arizona, December 1975).

"The Star of the Epiphany," *The Church Quarterly Review*, 144 (1947).

"Stars—Where Life Begins," *Time,* 108, no. 26 (December 27, 1976).

STOCKWELL, JOHN N., "Supplement to Recent Contributions to Chronology and Eclipses," *Astronomical Journal,* 12 (November 26, 1892).

STORRER, WILLIAM ALLIN, "When Was Christ Born?," *Harvard Magazine,* 77, no. 10 (June 1975).

SULLIVAN, WALTER, "New View on the Star of Bethlehem Suggests It was Stellar Flare-Up," *The New York Times* (December 17, 1977).

TINDALL, E. ABBEY, "The Star of Bethlehem," *The Expository Times,* 25 (October 1913).

"The True Date of Christ's Birth," trans. from Wieseler, *Chronologische Synopse der vier Evangelien,* Hamburg, 1843, by Rev. George E. Day, *Bibliotheca Sacra,* 3 (1846).

VAN DYKE, HENRY, "The Wise Men of the East," *The Mentor,* 13 (December 1925).

"The Visit of the Magi: the Time and Place of Its Occurrence," *The Journal of Sacred Literature,* 3d ser. 5 (1857).

"What Was the Star of Bethlehem?," *The Mentor,* 11 (December 1923).

"What Was the Star of Bethlehem?," *Christianity Today,* 9, no. 6 (December 18, 1964).

"Wise Men from the East," *The New York Times Magazine* (December 23, 1951).

WOOLSEY, REV. THEODORE D., "The Year of Christ's Birth," *Bibliotheca Sacra,* 27 (1870).

WRIGHT, HERBERT F., "Comets as Portents," *The American Catholic Quarterly Review,* 46 (1921).

WRIGHT, JULIA MAC NAIR, "The Real Star of Bethlehem," *Lippincott's Monthly Magazine,* 64 (1899).

WRIGHT, WILLIAM, "Eusebius of Caesarea on the Star," *The Journal of Sacred Literature,* 4th ser. 9 and 10 (1866).

WYLIE, C. C., "A Proposal for the Christmas Star," *Sky & Telescope,* 10 (December 1950).

ZAITSEV, VYACHESLAV, "Visitors from Outer Space," *Sputnik* (January 1967).

ZEITLIN, SOLOMON, "Bar Kokba and Bar Kozeba," *The Jewish Quarterly Review,* 43 (July 1952).